101 575 018 4

D0491966

Macmillan Building and Surveying Series
Series Editor: Ivor H. Seeley
Emeritus Professor, Nottingham Trent University

Series Standing Order (Macmillan Building and Surveying Series)

If you would like to receive future titles in this series as they are published, you can make use of our standing order facility. To place a standing order please contact your bookseller or, in case of difficulty, write to us at the address below with your name and address and the name of the series. Please state with which title you wish to begin your standing order. (If you live outside the United Kingdom we may not have the rights for your area, in which case we will forward your order to the publisher concerned.)

Customer Services Department, Macmillan Distribution Ltd
Houndmills, Basingstoke, Hampshire, RG21 6XS, England.

Value Management in Construction

A Practical Guide

Brian R. Norton

and

William C. McElligott

MACMILLAN

First published 1995 by
MACMILLAN PRESS LTD
Houndmills, Basingstoke, Hampshire RG21 6XS
and London
Companies and representatives
throughout the world

ISBN 0–333–60626–4

A catalogue record for this book is available
from the British Library.

10   9   8   7   6   5   4   3   2   1
04   03   02   01   00   99   98   97   96   95

Copy-edited and typeset by Povey-Edmondson
Okehampton and Rochdale, England

Printed in Great Britain by
Antony Rowe Ltd
Chippenham, Wiltshire

Contents

List of Figures

List of Working Documents

Acknowledgements

We owe a great deal of gratitude to all of those who have helped us to prepare this book. To Pam Skoutelas and Carol Read who tirelessly typed the text and to Chris Sexton who prepared some of the graphics. Our thanks are also extended to Andy Wheaton and John Grounds who provided the basis for the life cycle cost examples, to Currie Brown and in particular David Broomer for their support, to Lewis Anderson for his advice and to Brian Vawser and Andy Smith for their input.

Our appreciation also goes to Ivor Seeley for his editing and general advice, and to Macmillan Press and Malcolm Stewart in particular, for their support and guidance.

Thanks are also due to McGraw-Hill for permission to reproduce Figure 6.1, from A. J. Dell'Isola and S. J. Kirk, *Life Cycle Costing for Design Professionals* (1981).

Last, but definitely not least, our thanks to our wives Sheila and Barbara without whose patience, love and moral support this book would have never been accomplished.

August 1994

BRIAN R. NORTON
WILLIAM C. MCELLIGOTT

PART I

Introduction and Overview of VM

1 Introduction and Background to VM

1.1 Introduction

Intensifying competition caused by the globalisation of markets and other factors, together with ever-accelerating change has, in recent years, placed a growing importance of improving every facet of an organisation's operation.

Market globalisation has in effect led to increased competition, not just between companies, but also on a macro level, between individual countries. The need for improvement of organisational activities is thus felt not only in private industry but also increasingly in institutional, governmental or other non-profit organisations whose efficiency and effectiveness determine a country's competitive position in the world.

Keeping costs low with traditional cost management has been a commonly applied measure to improve competitiveness. However merely keeping costs down is not enough: there is an increasing need for not just efficiency but also for effectiveness. Here is where cost management and value management (VM) fundamentally differ. Whereas cost management seeks 'to do a thing right', i.e. efficiency, VM seeks 'to do the right thing', i.e. effectiveness.[1] No matter how efficiently a product or service is provided, it will not be successful unless it is *wanted*, i.e. it is effective. VM is thus arguably of greater importance than, and should *precede*, cost management efforts.

Construction, for many organisations, will represent a huge capital investment which translates into significant fixed costs for that organisation. These fixed costs have obvious ramifications for the prices of their products or services. Furthermore, such high fixed costs also represent a constraint upon an organisation's flexibility, which is a matter of increasing significance in today's rapidly changing world. VM should therefore first be applied to address the business strategy issue of whether the construction of a facility represents the best manner in which to meet the organisation's needs. Only after this investigation has resulted in a decision to build should VM then address the questions of 'what' should be constructed to meet the organisational needs and 'how' to most effectively and efficiently provide 'what' it is that is to be built.

---

1. Based on phraseology from P. Drucker, *Management* (Pan Books, 1979) p. 44.

As the intent of this book is to provide a practical guide to VM in construction, the emphasis is placed on the latter two applications of VM. The first application, whereby VM is used to assist in the process of deciding whether or not to build, is also covered in the book, but mainly to give an appreciation of how the applications integrate into an overall VM programme.

1.2   Background to VM

Origins

The forebear of value management, as we know it today, was developed during the Second World War at the General Electric Company in the USA. Owing to the shortages of raw materials caused by the war effort, General Electric was forced to use substitute materials in many of their products. Over time, it became evident that this forced substitution often resulted in lower product costs as well as improved product performance. Having recognised this phenomenon, General Electric sought to harness its potential for combined product performance improvement and cost reduction.

An electrical engineer, Mr Larry Miles, who was in General Electric's Purchasing Department under Mr Harry Erlicher, developed a formal procedure to derive the benefits noted from the forced substitution of materials during the war. The seeds of this procedure were spawned during the war when Larry Miles began to apply a functional approach to purchasing. This functional approach entailed the comparison of alternate materials based on the functions required to be performed by them.

The departure that function analysis represented from traditional approaches can perhaps best be explained by the following short story about a training course conducted by Larry Miles.

On that first morning, this bewildered novice entered a large room filled with the paraphernalia of a typical value workshop. I greeted other equally bewildered attendees as we all waited for the workshop to begin. At 9:00 a.m., the workshop started with the usual administrative announcements and introductions. Exactly one hour later, Mr Miles was introduced. He walked to the front of the room to begin the training. And what a beginning it was!

He held up a clock. 'How much is it worth?' he asked. We responded. 'Why is it worth $5?' he inquired. We were a very bright group. One of our more outspoken students took it upon himself to educate Mr Miles in the design and production of electric clocks and discussed in detail how the labour, materials and overheads incurred in the manufacture of the clock determined its value. Larry profusely thanked our self-appointed spokesman.

'How about the rest of you?' he asked, 'Do you agree?' We all nodded affirmatively. 'Well,' he said sagely, 'let's test your logic. Suppose I add some additional – very costly – labour to the clock. would that make it worth more?' We looked at each other. Of course it would. And again, we nodded in unison.

With that, Larry took a perfectly good clock and threw it against a wall as hard as he could. It was smashed to pieces. We were absolutely horrified! There was not a sound in the room. You could have heard the proverbial pin drop, had someone dared to drop one. Quietly he asked, 'Now what is the clock worth?' We were nonplussed. What was the answer?

Quietly Larry said, 'Function! The clock does something. Its value is determined by what it does. Its value is not related to its cost of manufacture.'

For forty students, that smashed clock represented a new understanding of the concept of value and a new beginning for each of us as we became better acquainted with the precepts of Value Analysis during the next three weeks. Three decades later that smashed clock remains perfectly vivid in my memory and helped to etch indelibly in my mind as in the minds of thousands of others, the meaning of value.   (O'Brien, 1976, pp. 25–6)

Miles expanded on the function approach between 1947 and 1952 and combined a series of steps and techniques into one procedure which was called Value Analysis (VA). Value analysis initially expanded beyond the General Electric Company when a representative of the US Navy, who had attended a value analysis workshop at General Electric, recommended that the procedure should be applied in the Navy Bureau of Ships. This recommendation was accepted and the Navy Bureau of Ships initiated their value program in 1954. While General Electric had been applying this value analysis procedure retrospectively on existing products, the Navy took a more proactive approach and started using the procedure during the design or engineering stages. Thus emerged the name of 'Value Engineering' (VE) to describe the procedure applied during design stages. Over time the use of VE spread to other divisions of the Department of Defense and via incentive clauses to their suppliers and contractors from private industry.

The combined growth in VE practice through different government agencies and private industry led to the establishment of the Society of American Value Engineers (SAVE) in 1958, a professional body formed to foster VE.

VE first entered the construction industry in the early 1960s when VE incentive provisions were included in construction contracts. These provisions would encourage contractors to suggest alternatives that would reduce a construction project's costs without adversely impacting on its functional aspects. The savings from contractors' proposals were often shared between the owner and contractor.

During the late 1960s and early 1970s VE began to be used during the design stages of construction projects by some government agencies such as the Facilities Division of the National Aeronautics and Space Agency (NASA) and the General Services Administration (GSA).

The application of VE during the design phases of construction has grown to such an extent that it is perhaps in this application that VE is now most often utilised in the USA.

Over the past decade, there has been a trend toward applying value techniques at ever-earlier stages in a project's life cycle. To distinguish this activity, the term 'Value Planning' has arisen in a growing number of organisations to describe more strategic-type value studies undertaken at early conceptual design stages. In addition, the term 'Value Management' (VM) has become a blanket term that covers all value techniques whether they entail Value Planning, Value Engineering or Value Analysis.

The scope for the application of VM is continually expanding, and in 1994 there were two bills under review by the US Congress that, if enacted, will considerably impact the utilisation of VM in the USA. The first provides Federal incentives to State transportation agencies employing VM. With current highway expenditure at approximately $30 billion per annum, this could have a considerable impact on overall demand for VM.

Even more significant is the bill which proposes to make VM mandatory on all government 'programs, projects, systems, and products comprising the aggregate 80% of the budget of the agency'. Under this bill, VM would not merely be applicable to construction expenditure but to all government expenditure of any nature. With annual government expenditure of over $1000 billion, the success of this Bill could produce an explosive demand for VM in the USA.

Whether these bills are passed or not, the growth of VM in the USA and the trend towards earlier, and more widespread, applications looks set to continue.

Overseas Expansion of VM

Since the 1960s, and perhaps earlier, VM expanded beyond US borders throughout the world. It was particularly well received by the Japanese who purportedly utilise the procedure extensively in the automotive and electronics industries in which they have been so successful. VM is also known to be utilised increasingly in other Far Eastern countries such as Korea and China and in Asian countries such as India. There is significant application of VM in Australia and in Middle East countries such as Saudi Arabia and Kuwait.

In Europe, there are established VA associations in the UK, Germany, France, Belgium, Italy, the Netherlands, Portugal and Spain and VA activity in Denmark, Ireland and Greece.

A study commissioned by SPRINT (a European community programme for innovation and technology transfer), published in 1992, forecast growing utilisation of VA throughout Europe, at about 13% per annum. In the UK, the

Institute of Value Management (see Appendix 2, p. 221 for address) succeeded the Value Engineering Association which had been established in 1966.

VA and VM are used in the UK by electronics, general engineering, aerospace, automotive, construction and increasingly by service industries. The application of VM in construction appears to have commenced during the early 1980s and has seen significant growth over recent years with public authorities, as well as organisations from private industry, instigating VM activities in connection with their construction programmes.

As in the USA, there appears to be increasing activity in the earlier VP areas as well as the in more traditional VE activities, and it seems that this trend is likely to continue as the more general use of VM expands.

VM has been successfully applied on all types of construction, from buildings to offshore oil and gas platforms, and for all types of clients from private industry to governmental organisations.

1.3   Key Terms

The approach taken when using VM techniques differs according to the stage of the project life cycle at which it is applied. It is thus useful to differentiate between the types of approach appropriate to each stage by defining them with different terms.

At the time of this writing there are no universally accepted definitions, and a number of different definitions have arisen to describe the same approach or stage of application. While it is not essential to adhere to a common terminology, conflicting terms for the same activity can sometimes cause confusion. A fairly common practice has been to describe early strategic applications of value techniques as VM studies as opposed to later tactical applications which are described as VE studies. This may cause confusion as the term 'VM' is also applied as a broad, higher order, description which encompasses all value techniques, whether applied at the strategic or tactical level.

In order to prevent the possibility of such confusion, we have used the terminologies which have developed as described in the foregoing section on the background of VM and which have been applied both in the UK and USA. These terminologies, which are described below, are adhered to throughout the book.

Value Management (VM) is the title given to the full range of value techniques available. It is a higher order title and is not linked to a particular project stage at which value techniques may be applied.

Value Planning (VP) is the title given to value techniques applied during the 'planning' phases of a project. Thus, VP studies are those conducted during the Briefing or Sketch Plan stages of the Royal Institute of British Architects (RIBA) plan of work. This term may be further subdivided to include Strategic VP which is a term that can be applied to the earliest business strategy-type study applied during, or prior to, the feasibility stage of the RIBA plan of work when alternatives to a built solution will be considered. For those readers who have come across the use of the term VM to describe these early studies, Strategic VP and VP studies are the equivalent of studies that are frequently denoted as VM1 and VM2.

(*Value Engineering* (VE) is the title given to value techniques applied during the design or 'engineering' phases of a project.)Thus, VE studies are those conducted during the early part of the Working Drawings stage of the RIBA plan of work. Where subcontracts include an element of design, smaller scale VE activities may also occur during the Construction stage.

(*Value Analysis* (VA) is the title given to value techniques applied retrospectively to completed projects to 'analyse' or audit the project's performance.) Thus, VA studies are those conducted during the post-construction period and may be a part of a Post-Occupancy Evaluation exercise. In addition, the term VA may be applied to the analysis of non-construction related procedures and processes, such as studies of organisational structure, or procurement procedures, etc.

The different stages of the RIBA plan of work at which the various studies are undertaken are indicated in Working Document 1.1.

1.4   Book Outline and Intent

The basic intent of this book is to provide practical guidance with regard to the application of the VM methodology. The book goes beyond merely describing the theory of VM in order to explain how the methodology can be productively used in practice. It is hoped that the practical advice contained in its chapters will assist readers, who are involved with establishing VM activities within their organisations, to do so effectively. It is also aimed at assisting all those who may become involved with VM to participate more productively by giving them a greater appreciation of the basics of VM, and how it relates to other construction activities.

The readership audience targeted may thus be split into two main categories:

- Those from private and public organisations involved with, or interested in, establishing VM within their organisation
- Students and practitioners from the various disciplines, such as Architects, Engineers, Cost Consultants and so on, who may become involved in VM activities .

Rather than providing equal coverage to all topics, we have emphasised the basics of VM in this book. We have thus concentrated on the application of

Working Document 1.1   Typical terms for VM studies at different stages

VALUE MANAGEMENT		
VALUE PLANNING (Strategic)	VALUE ENGINEERING	VALUE ANALYSIS

RIBA PLAN OF WORK

BRIEFING		SKETCH PLANS		WORKING DRAWINGS				CONSTRUCTION	POST-CONSTRUCTION
Inception	Feasibility	Outline Proposals	Scheme Design	Detail Design	Production Information	Bills of Quantities	Tender Action	Construction	Post-Occupancy Evaluation

AIA PLAN OF WORK

CONCEPT		SCHEMATIC	PRODUCTION			CONSTRUCTION	POST-CONSTRUCTION
Programming	Progrm Evaluation	Schematic Design	Design Development	Construction Documents	Bidding Action	Construction	Post-Occupancy Evaluation

Key:
RIBA: Royal Institute of British Architects.
AIA: American Institute of Architects.

the later VP and VE studies in Part II describing the VM process, Since the majority of readers will be involved with these types of studies. In addition, the methodology applied in such studies forms the basis for that which is applied during earlier Strategic VP studies, and it is important to understand these basics before moving on to the more advanced applications of VM associated with Strategic VP studies.

In terms of structure, the book is split into four parts.

Part I provides an introduction and overview of VM which is intended to place the methodology in context.

Part II provides a detailed description of the practical activities involved in the VM process and forms, in essence, the core of the book. As explained above, this section describes the VM methodology applied during later VP and VE, studies as opposed to that applied to early Strategic VP studies. The term 'VM' used in the context of this part of the book should be read to mean either VP or VE.

Part III covers other issues involved with VM. Chapter 10 describes the practical issues involved with establishing and running a VM programme. Chapter 11 describes how Strategic VP studies differ from those described in Part II as well as describing how VM relates to other project management activities. Lastly Chapter 12 provides contact details for professional VM bodies and describes typical VM training activities.

Finally Part IV provides full Case Studies of VP and VE exercises for various project types. While practical examples associated with a wide variety of projects are interspersed throughout the book, the Case Studies in Part IV provide comprehensive examples which cover all stages of the VM process for each project.

2 Overview of the VM Process

2.1 Introduction

This chapter serves as a broad overview of the Value Management (VM) process. This skeletal outline is fleshed out with more detail in subsequent chapters to provide a comprehensive understanding of many practical aspects of VM.

This chapter may be used as an effective introduction to VM for those readers seeking detailed information on the practical aspects included in later chapters, or may merely be utilised as an executive summary for those desiring merely a broad overview of the process. Readers in the latter category may include senior management who are in a position to recommend and instigate new ventures such as VM within their organisations.

The contents of this chapter cover the following five key areas:

- What VM is, and what it is not
- When to use VM
- What is necessary for VM to be successful
- How authentic VM is performed
- Why VM is effective.

2.2 What VM Is and What It Is Not

Most people involved in construction work believe they know what VM is. Generally, they apply the term to any methodology used to seek ways to reduce costs. While VM does usually result in cost reduction, it is very different from all other cost reduction techniques applied to construction projects. Others believe VM is something that designers routinely do during design development process. This belief is equally false.

Definition of True VM

VM may be defined as:

> A *systematic, multi-disciplinary* effort directed toward analysing the *functions* of projects for the purpose of achieving the best *value* at the lowest overall *life cycle project cost.*

This definition contains five key words and/or phrases. The following explanation of these five points will serve to provide a better understanding of how true VM is distinguished from simple cost reduction activities.

The application of VM involves a very **systematic** process which is known as the job plan. It has a definite beginning and a definite end. In that respect it differs from simple cost reduction exercises, which are normally informal and very unstructured.

A VM study is a **multi-disciplinary** effort. It involves bringing together as a team, a group of individuals who collectively are able to **authoritatively** analyse all aspects of the project under study. They work together as a group under the direction of a Value Management Team Coordinator (VMTC) who leads them through the VM job plan. During this process, each member of the team is encouraged to participate in discussions, not just in their own areas of expertise, but in every area being studied. By working together as a team, the individuals support each other. Virtually every project involves the blending together of various disciplines since no one individual is expert in every area involved in a construction project. However, many of these areas overlap with one another. A decision made in one discipline can have a profound impact on another. In a typical cost cutting exercise each discipline often conducts its own independent review and many times the impact of their proposals on other disciplines is not adequately considered. By using a multi- disciplinary team approach this problem is avoided.

Another benefit derived from the multi-disciplinary approach is that some of the best ideas for project improvements or for cost reductions frequently emanate from an individual who is not of the discipline to which the idea relates. While that individual, on his own, would not be able to properly develop the idea because of his lack of expertise in that particular discipline, in a multi-disciplinary team approach that is not a problem.

VM also involves analysing the **functions** of a project. This is an aspect of VM that is unique and which further distinguishes VM from other design review or cost reduction activities. Typically, in a cost reduction process the entire emphasis is on finding substitutes for various elements in a design. Thus, in cost reduction exercises, two questions are generally asked. The first is 'What is it?' and the second is 'What else can we use?'. Function analysis asks an additional question. Before it asks what may we substitute it asks 'What does it do? or 'What is the function that it seeks to achieve? Only after this has been determined are alternative solutions sought. The following Case Example shows how this can help to gain a better understanding of the problem at hand, and how this in turn can afford better solutions.

Case Example

An analysis of a mousetrap demonstrates how function analysis can open up a broad range of alternatives that can lead to better solutions. In a typical cost reduction process the review of a mousetrap's design would proceed immediately into alternative ways to trap mice. In a VM process, a function analysis would first be performed. Typically, when individuals are asked to define the function of a mousetrap their response is that the function is to catch or trap mice. However, that is not the function of a mousetrap. In order to determine the true function you must first ask the question *Why?*. When that question is asked the answer is usually to eliminate mice. That is the 'real' function of a mousetrap. By determining this true function it then becomes clear that there is a broader scope of solutions to the problem of elimination of mice other than just trapping them. When asked for alternative solutions a team will come up with a variety of answers which may include ideas such as getting a cat, changing the environment in some way to make it unattractive to mice, using something like high frequency sound or, of course, using some form of poison.

It can be seen that by first asking the question *Why?* a far broader scope of alternative solutions to the problem can be identified.

The next key word in the definition is **value**. In a VM study, the object is not to reduce cost, the object is to improve value. Figure 2.1 shows that cost is just one element relative to value on a construction project. Two other important aspects are time and function or quality. In order to achieve value, which in Figure 2.1 is depicted as being contained within an isosceles triangle, it is necessary to achieve a proper balance between all of the important aspects which make up a project's design.

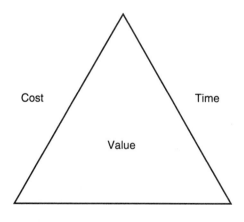

Figure 2.1   *Elements of value*

There are three major ways to improve value by applying VM:

- To provide for all the required project functions but at a reduced cost
- To provide additional desirable project functions without adding to the cost
- To provide additional desirable project functions while at the same time reducing costs.

Although perhaps surprising to the uninitiated, the latter is the most common result of a VM study. In some cases VM proposals result in changes to design elements which, in and of themselves, represent improvements while also representing cost reductions. For example, the simplification of an item of equipment may ease use while also reducing cost. In other cases, the cost reductions derived from deletions or modifications that do not compromise project functions can then be used to provide for enhancements in other areas of design. In both cases it can be seen that it is not incongruous to state that VM frequently results in project enhancements while at the same time reducing costs.

While the definition on p. 11 stresses seeking the best value for the project, it is not claimed that VM will necessarily find the 'optimum' solution. Such an optimum would be difficult to define. However, by defining the best value as the goal, any movement towards that goal will represent an improvement. Human nature, which ultimately also determines organisational behaviour, is often of a 'satisficing' type. This means that once a satisfactory solution is found for a problem there is a tendency to forgo any further efforts aimed at improving that solution. VM overcomes this natural tendency by forcing us to consider improvements to what may already be a good and satisfactory solution.

In a VM study, the focus is not just on initial capital costs. The focus is more correctly applied to total **life cycle costs** which comprise the initial costs of construction together with the present value of the costs associated with using the final facility, such as operating and maintenance costs. As the costs in use frequently far outweigh initial capital costs when considered over the life of the facility, it can be seen that life cycle costing (LCC) typically represents a more realistic appraisal of the full cost of design solutions. This, then, is another aspect of VM which distinguishes it from other design review practices.

Test for Authentic VM

A simple test can be applied in order to distinguish between authentic VM and services which some may describe as VM, but which are in fact nothing more than cost cutting exercises. For a service or activity to be characterised as authentic VM, there are four criteria which must be satisfied.

The first is that it must follow an *approved VM job plan*. While there are a variety of job plans applied by different organisations, they all broadly follow a standard five step job plan which is described later in this chapter. The additional steps included in the other job plans merely represent subdivisions of some of the steps in the traditional five step job plan. The majority of authentic VM studies conducted apply the five step job plan, and its constituent phases should be clearly distinguishable for an activity to be considered as VM.

The second criterion is that the study should involve a *multi-disciplinary team working* together in the same place at the same time, as explained earlier in the chapter.

Thirdly, a VM study should be facilitated or led by a qualified *Value Management Team Coordinator* (VMTC), whose function it is to act as a facilitator and guide the multi-disciplinary team through the formal job plan.

Besides the tangible aspects of coordinating and controlling the activities during the VM studies, a qualified Value Specialist is also trained in *intangible skills* such as team building. It is often these intangible aspects that can make the difference between the success and failure of a study.

At the time of writing, the British Institute of Value Management (IVM) is currently developing a certification procedure which should help to establish the credentials of those purporting to offer VM services. A number of individuals in the UK have gained the qualification of Certified Value Specialist (CVS) from the Society of American Value Engineers. While it is not necessarily imperative for the VMTC to be qualified as a value specialist, it is a good indication that authentic VM will be practised if the team leader has these credentials.

Finally, and probably the most important criterion, is that in the review process true VM does not pursue any design changes which detract from the project's required or basic functions. This is generally assured through the formal application of *function analysis techniques*, which are described in detail later in this book.

2.3   When to use VM

The basic reason to use VM is because there are almost always elements involved in a project which contribute to poor value. The ones listed and explained below are by no means a complete list: virtually anyone involved with VM could easily add to this classification.

Factors which Contribute to Poor Value

1   *Not enough time to do the job*
     As discussed previously, one of the elements which must be in balance with other project aspects in order to achieve value is the *programme*.

The programme must be in balance with cost concerns and all other project concerns. Sometimes in a project a very demanding programme requires the design team to move forward without crossing all the t's and dotting all the i's. This, of course, will result in unnecessary costs and possibly design errors.

2   *Habitual thinking*

We are all creatures of habit, and this does not disappear when we are acting in the capacity of designers. When a solution that we have used in the past works, we will all have a tendency to repeat the solution any time we encounter the same problem. However, the state of the art in technology is constantly changing and whilst the previously applied solution will work in a particular situation there might be better solutions that have been developed. When a VM team hears something like 'I've always done it this way' they will immediately be alerted to the fact that there is a potential problem. What the team must be attuned to is whether or not the individual making such a statement has many years of experience or, in fact, *one* year of experience *many times over.*

3   *Poor communications*

Determining project requirements at the onset of the design effort is a long, arduous and tedious task which is fraught with opportunities for *misinterpretation* and *miscommunication.* If a member of the design team misunderstands a requirement described by a user he can make errors in achieving what it is that the user really wants.

4   *Lack of coordination between the designer and operations' personnel*

This, unfortunately, is a very common problem. While a client will usually assign an individual to act in a liaisonary capacity with the design team, it is not always the case that that individual will be a good representative of the people who will have to *operate* the facility after it is completed.

5   *Outdated standards or specifications*

Again, this is a rather frequent problem. Most organizations do not have the capacity to continuously *update* their standards and specifications and, thus, they can easily become outdated. Design solutions that were reasonable and practical five or ten years ago could easily be extremely inefficient and ineffective in the current design environment.

6   *Absence of state of the art technology*

New products and design tools are constantly appearing in the market. It is virtually impossible for all members of the design team to keep up to the minute in their respective disciplines. A VM team which contains independent members will have a different group of experts who will also have their own shortcomings, but it would be unusual for both individuals in a particular area of expertise to have the same deficiencies.

7   *Honest false beliefs*

It is not infrequent for an individual who is part of the design team to follow a particular course in his design effort because he thought it was necessary to achieve a particular requirement which, in fact, is *not required* at all.

8   *Prejudicial thinking*
A typical example of this is the situation when a member of the design group tried something in the past and it did not work, and, therefore, has never tried it again. However, it is very possible that the reasons why that particular design solution did not work in the past was due to a set of circumstances that *does not exist* in the current design problem.

9   *Lack of needed experts*
With the continually increasing complexity of technology a very wide variety of expertise is required on many different types of projects. Sometimes a design team must address this problem by using an individual from the group who is an expert in one area and is only partially familiar in another area to handle that other area. The usual practice in a situation like this is to deal with the problem by *over-designing*.

10   *Unnecessarily restrictive design criteria*
A typical example of this is where temperature and humidity regimes may be unduly narrow for no particular reason. If such criteria are not questioned by the designers these restrictions may impose unnecessary cost.

11   *Scope of changes for missing items*
At an advanced stage of design, or during construction, if it is found that a required element is missing from the project it is very expensive to add that item and, thus, contributes to *poor value*.

12   *Lack of needed information*
When required information is not available to a design team they have to continue the design process by working around the element requiring the missing information. This can lead to the inclusion of *unnecessary cost items* which are included simply to take care of the unknown.

Type of Projects that Benefit Most from VM

There are costs associated with VM, therefore it is probably impractical to use it on every project. However, it is probably a good idea to apply VM if any one of the following is the case on a particular project:

1   *Costly projects*
Since VM will usually result in cost savings in the order of 5–10%, or in many cases higher percentages, applying VM to high cost projects is almost always cost effective.

2   *Complex projects*
A VM study affords an opportunity to get expert second opinions. When using VM team members who are independent from the original design

team for very technically complex projects, getting a second opinion is almost always an excellent idea.

3   *Repetitive costs*
When an organisation is involved with repetitive type construction projects, those which they tend to build many times in various locations, the utilisation of VM is usually very cost effective because the cost reduction ideas can be incorporated in each of the later projects of the same type.

4   *Unique projects with few precedents or with new technology elements*
This is a very similar situation to complex projects. Again, the benefit of VM is in achieving an expert second opinion when independent team members are included.

5   *Projects with very restricted construction budgets*
With projects of this type it is imperative to achieve maximum value for money. Since, by definition, VM seeks to achieve the elimination of unnecessary costs, its application on projects with tight budgets is usually a very good idea.

6   *Projects with compressed design programmes*
The old saying 'haste makes waste' is especially true with regard to construction projects. Whilst VM is an added requirement which can have a tendency to add to a project's programme, this time can be minimised if the VM activity is properly coordinated with the design programme.

7   *High visibility projects*
This situation applies particularly to government sponsored or environmentally sensitive construction projects. If errors or problems develop on a project they tend to be seized upon by the media and used to embarrass the officials involved. Again, because VM provides an opportunity to obtain expert second opinions it is a very effective tool for avoiding problems of this nature.

Selecting the Optimum Projects for Study

For organisations with large construction programmes, which include a large number of projects, a form of analysis is necessary to determine which projects in the programme should be selected for VM. VM employs an analytical technique which is derived from Paretos Law of Maldistribution which states that it can usually be assumed that one can find 80% of all costs in just 20% of the items involved. If this is applied to analyse an organization's capital construction programme it can provide effective criteria for selecting those projects which offer the greatest opportunity for the benefit which VM offers. The charts shown in Figure 2.2 demonstrate how this technique was applied in the New York City construction programme. Figure 2.2 shows that the City's capital programme over a four year period included over almost 5000 individual capital projects with a total cost of approximately $19 billion.

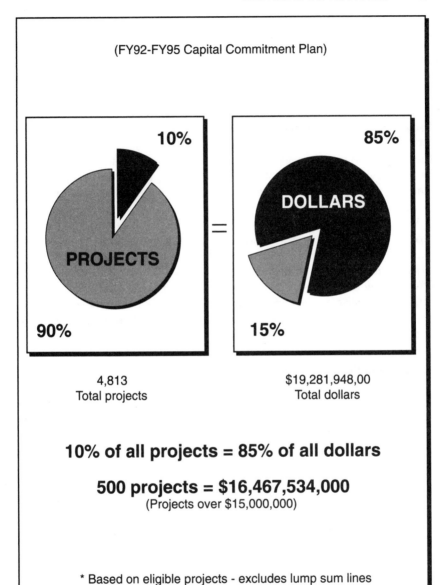

(FY92-FY95 Capital Commitment Plan)

10%

85%

DOLLARS

=

PROJECTS

90%

15%

4,813
Total projects

$19,281,948,00
Total dollars

10% of all projects = 85% of all dollars

500 projects = $16,467,534,000
(Projects over $15,000,000)

* Based on eligible projects - excludes lump sum lines

*Figure 2.2   Using Pareto's Law to select projects: New York City VM programme,
1992–95*

In a computer analysis it was determined that 10% of the projects (or approximately 500 projects) contained 85% of the dollar value in the capital programme, i.e. $16.5 billion. The City was thus able to select those projects which would be the best candidates for VM review by focusing on just those 500 projects.

Use of VM even when Problems are not Evident

Cost reduction exercises are only employed once budgetary problems have become evident. Even typical cost management techniques such as cost planning may not be as keenly focused where projects are running smoothly as when cost overruns are forecast.

VM, however, affords an opportunity to reduce costs and improve the project even if there are no obvious problems. It overcomes the potentially wasteful attitude common to many that 'if it ain't broke, don't fix it'. Even when there is no cost problem there is no harm in eliminating unnecessary cost anyway and releasing those funds for either project enhancements or other capital projects. VM can also be used to intervene at strategic milestone points to make sure that a project is staying on track with respect to cost, time and quality or functional requirements.

VM and Traditional Cost Management

It should be understood that even when effective traditional cost management is being used on a project, such as is the case when quantity surveyors (QSs) have been employed to manage project costs, using VM is still an excellent idea because the two activities are completely synergistic. A QS provides ongoing day to day cost management while a VM team review provides detailed, expert, in depth analysis at milestone points. One does not replace the other: the VM team can provide a menu of cost reduction proposals and, after the VM team leaves the scene, the QS can make sure that the VM proposals are in fact implemented in the design. Rather than replace each other, the two activities supplement each other.

2.4   What Is Necessary For VM To Be Successful?

VM programmes have a checquered history. For the most part, VM programmes are successful in that they produce desired results. On the other hand, some programmes never really get off the ground. The difference between the two is that the successful programmes are given the elements that they need to be successful while the unsuccessful programmes die off because they are never given the support elements needed.

The single most critical element in a VM programme is *top level support*. Adding VM to a design process is a new departure from the traditional way of doing things. As with most new departures, it represents change and people tend to resist change. In order to get VM off to a good start, this natural opposition must be overcome. The only way that this is possible is if top level management clearly indicates that they fully support the VM programme, wish it to be successful and require their staff to cooperate fully with this new venture.

The next consideration relates to where to *locate* the VM activity within the parent organisation. In order for VM to be effective it must be independent of the design department since it should not be subject to any particular bias. This is virtually impossible if the VM staff reports to the unit which is responsible for design because, in effect, this puts the VM staff in the position of having to critique the work completed by their superiors. Ideally VM should be located in a unit that is responsible for projects from an overall perspective. The unit should be concerned about achieving all the important aspects of a project. Primarily this would mean that they would be concerned with not just cost but also time, as well as project quality or scope.

The next need is for *resources*. These take two forms. There must be an allocation of resources for the necessary fees for consultants, and, there must also be an allocation of resources for the in-house management activities that are necessary in order to keep the VM process moving along.

Finally, management of the VM activities should not be totally controlled by any *one unit* in an organization. Others who will be affected by the decisions resulting from VM reviews should participate in the planning activities, the actual workshops, as well as the decision process relative to the proposals which come out of the VM studies. The group of individuals should include someone responsible for cost management, someone from design and a representative from the unit that will be required to operate the facility once it is completed.

2.5   How Authentic VM is Performed

Approaches to VM

There are four basic approaches, and permutations on those approaches, by which VM can be implemented. They are:

1   An in-house programme in which all of the team members as well as the VMTC are employees of the organisation
2   In-house team members and an external VMTC or facilitator
3   In-house team members supplemented by experts who cannot be provided by the in-house organization as well as an external VMTC or facilitator

4   A predominantly external group of individuals to conduct the VM study. The group would consist of all of the members of the VM team as well as the VMTC or facilitator together with some in-house representation.

Each of the approaches may be appropriate in different circumstances. In general, VM studies undertaken in the UK tend to favour approach 3 in which predominantly in-house teams are used, whereas in the USA approach 4, whereby the team is predominantly external, is most commonly applied. The basic trade off between the two approaches is between the ease of implementation encouraged by in-house and project team participation and the objectivity gained through the participation of external VM team members. This is explained in further detail in Chapter 3.

The VM Procedure

The systematic procedure applied during a VM study, whether a VP or VE study, encompasses the three distinct phases of Pre-study, Workshop or Study, and Post-study activities, which are now described in turn.

Pre-study phase   The primary concerns of the Pre-study phase are that all parties are well coordinated and that there is ample information available for review during the VM Study.

Generally an orientation meeting is held between the Value Specialists and relevant client and/or design team representatives to establish the logistics for the study and to inform the Value Specialists of project issues and constraints so that the study may be properly targeted. In addition to compiling information such as design drawings, geotechnical surveys, client brief, etc. the Value Specialist will translate any cost estimate information available into easily understood *cost models*. During the study these cost models can be used to focus on high cost areas.

Study or workshop phase   During this phase the multi-disciplinary team is mobilised to conduct the VM study following the procedure set down in the five step job plan subsequently described.

The team structure is tailored to suit the particular project type, but generally includes a VMTC (qualified Value Specialist or equivalent), relevant design professionals such as architect, mechanical, electrical, structural and other engineers, operations experts, quantity surveyor/cost engineer and client and user representatives. Where constructability and sequencing issues are of concern a construction manager may also participate. The optimal team size is generally recognised to be between six and twelve members; overly large teams should be avoided. Standard industry practice in the USA is to utilise teams that are independent of the design team, although in the UK there is a tendency to favour the use of the design team to undertake the study.

The duration of the study depends on the nature and size of the project and the stage at which the study is conducted. Studies are generally of three to six days duration, but may be divided into parts and extend to a number of weeks if the project is large and/or complex, or if it is simply impractical to start and finish without interruption.

The five step job plan comprises the following:

- Information phase
- Creative phase
- Evaluation phase
- Development phase
- Presentation phase.

Information phase   The objective of this phase is to establish a good understanding of the project, its design and operation, the function(s) of the project itself, and its constituent elements, and to determine areas with the greatest potential for savings and needed improvements.

To that end, the workshop generally starts with an overview of the activities which will occur during the VM process by the Value Specialist. This will be followed by design presentations from the design team. These activities are followed by the function analysis part of the Information phase. Function analysis is intended to assure that every VM team member fully understands all of the project's functional requirements, not just his or her own area of specialty – first by examining the total project and then each of its component elements, to identify their *basic* and *secondary functions*.

Creative phase   This phase can include any of various creativity/motivational techniques to generate alternative ideas to achieve the same basic function(s) at lower costs or to achieve necessary improvements. The most often used method is the *brainstorming technique*, which consists of the VM team generating and recording a large number of ideas without evaluation. (Idea evaluation is performed in the Evaluation phase.) The entire VM team participates in this session, so that ideas covering all disciplines are generated, even by participants in areas other than their own discipline.

The aim is to obtain quantity and association of ideas, to eliminate blocks that thwart creative thinking, and to allow a free flow of ideas.

Evaluation phase   Various evaluation methods may be used during this phase to analyse and highlight the best ideas generated during the Creative phase. Since there are usually time constraints on the number of ideas that can be properly developed, it is important that only the *best* ideas are selected. These ideas are evaluated, both on economic and non-economic criteria such as aesthetics, environmental impact, etc.

Development phase   The ideas for alternatives selected during the Evaluation phase are now developed into fully detailed proposals which generally comprise:

- Descriptions of both the original and the proposed revised design
- A narrative on the advantages and disadvantages of each proposal
- Initial and life cycle cost consequences of the proposals
- Detailed technical calculations, sketches, etc. which are necessary to fully describe the VM proposal.

Proposals must be detailed and avoid ambiguity otherwise they may be rejected with little consideration by decision makers. The process of developing detailed proposals also forces team members to consider all the ramifications of their ideas. If, during this consideration, it becomes apparent that any advantages are outweighed by disadvantages, the proposal is dropped.

Presentation phase   Generally, on the last day of the study a presentation of the refined and developed proposals will be made to decision makers and other interested parties. The proposals generated by the VM team will be summarised and the life cycle cost savings presented. The VM team members will present the rationale behind each of the recommendations presented. Draft copies of summaries of the proposals may be handed over so that decision makers can immediately commence evaluation of the recommendations.

Post-study phase   Within five to ten working days a preliminary VM report may be submitted which will contain all the detailed proposals and summaries, narratives on the VM process and so on. Concurrently with the report preparation, and for a period after its issuance, decision makers will consider the recommendations from the VM team.

Following an appropriate period for review, an implementation meeting should be held to determine whether proposals are to be accepted or rejected, and to establish subsequent actions.

Timing of Studies

VM Studies are generally timed so that they coincide with the end of a particular design phase. In this way, the study can occur concurrently with other reviews undertaken at those stages and thus minimise disruption and abortive design costs.

In general terms, the earlier in the design process that the study is undertaken the higher the cost reduction potential and the lower the abortive design costs and costs of implementation, as shown in Figure 2.3.

Ideally a VM programme for a project will include a combination of VP and VE studies.

A short VP study may occur at the end of the Briefing stage to review overall project requirements. It is perhaps more common to conduct a VP study during the Sketch Plans phase, when the basic early design becomes available for review.

The VP Study is intended to review '*what*' is to be built to satisfy the client's requirements. As it is conducted during the early stage of the project, broad aspects of the project may be challenged and altered without excessive abortive design costs. It is the VP study that normally achieves the best VM results.

A VE study will normally be conducted when all aspects of the design are defined, i.e. during the Detail Design stage. If the project is large, further VE studies may also be conducted.

The VE study is intended to review '*how*' the client's requirements are met. It involves a more detailed review of the components of the project to determine whether the design of various elements may be improved. While the results are not normally as highly rewarding as a VP study, the savings and improvements achieved can still be very significant. An approximate guideline target is for 5% or more cost savings without compromising direct project functions.

Finally, minor VE studies may be undertaken during construction by, or with, trade contractors and sub contractors with a design element in their contract and a VA study may be conducted for Post-Occupancy Evaluation purposes. These latter types of VM studies are, however, relatively uncommon.

2.6   Why VM is Effective

Figure 2.4 shows how the cost of VM is minimal compared to the cost of a construction project. Generally it can be expected that the cost of VM will be considerably less than 1% of the total construction project cost. Since it can be expected that a fairly well administered VM programme should yield cost reductions in the order of 5–10% of construction projects, it can be seen that VM literally pays for itself.

26

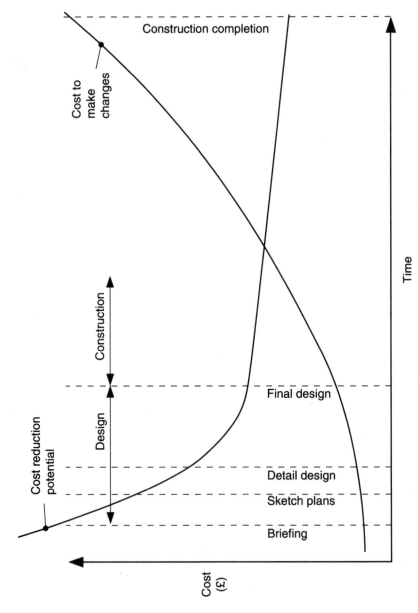

Figure 2.3   *Cost reduction potential versus cost to implement changes*

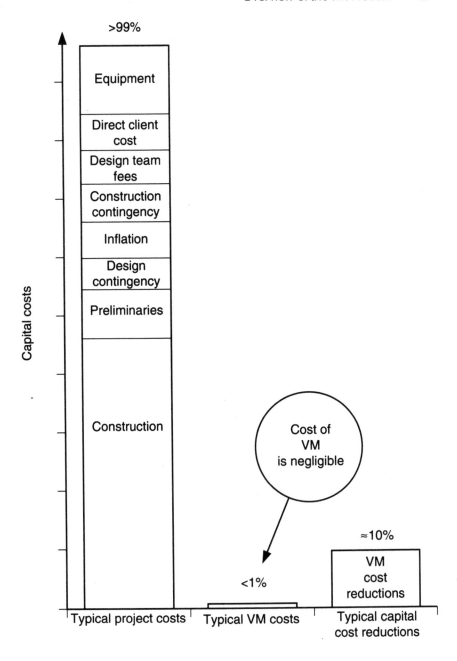

Figure 2.4 Cost of VM versus project costs

Despite being a relatively small investment compared to its potential return, VM, to some degree, helps to address the imbalance between the amount of expenditure on design at various stages relative to the amount of final cost of the project determined by that stage in design. Figure 2.5 shows clearly that there is relatively low expenditure on early design when most of the final cost of the project is committed, while there is greater expenditure during later design stages when the final cost has largely been established by prior decisions.

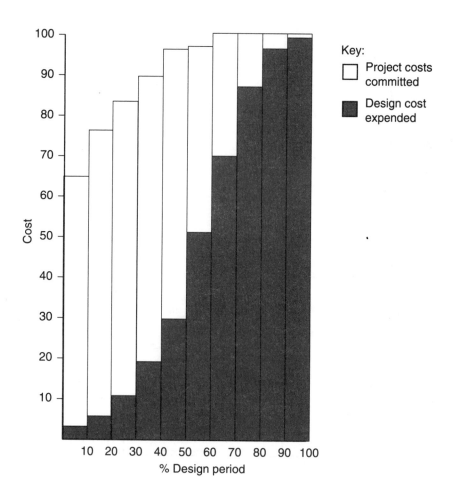

Figure 2.5   *Imbalance between timing of design expenditure versus time at which project costs are committed by the design*

Benefits of VM

Of course, the main reason for VM is that it results in many benefits to a project. The following provides a very brief list of such benefits:

- 1 Provides a *forum* for all concerned parties in a project development
- 2 Provides an *authoritative review* of the *entire* project, not just a few elements
- 3 Identifies *project constraints*, *issues* and *problems* which might not otherwise have been identified
- 4 Deals with *life cycle*, not just initial, costs
- 5 Usually results in remedying project *deficiencies* and *omissions* and *superfluous* items
- 6 Identifies and removes *unnecessary costs*
- 7 Provides a means to identify and incorporate project *enhancements*
- 8 Crystallises an organisation's brief or project *priorities*
- 9 Provides management with the information it needs to make *informed decisions*
- 10 Permits a *large return* on a minimal investment.

Competitive advantages.

PART II

Activities Involved in VM

3 Pre-study Phase

3.1 Introduction

The man who is prepared, has his battle half fought.   (*Don Quixote*)

The main objective of the Pre-study phase is to ensure that all parties are well coordinated, that the study is properly targeted and that there is sufficient pertinent information available for the actual study.

Distinct activities that occur during this phase include:

- Orientation meeting
- Finalising the team structure
- Selecting the team members
- Deciding on study duration
- Determining study location and conditions
- Gathering information
- Site visit
- Cost estimate verification
- Preparation of models and efficiency data.

These activities are each described in this chapter.

3.2 Orientation Meeting

It is always useful to have an orientation meeting a week or two prior to the study. The meeting would normally be attended by the VMTC, one or two key VM team members, client representatives and design team representatives. The purpose is to establish a preliminary understanding of the *project* and the client's *objectives*, so that information required for the study can be assessed and study logistics arranged. The meeting also serves as an occasion when the VMTC can get to know the constraints under which the design has been produced and discover the boundaries, political or otherwise, for the scope of the study.

Discussion may include strategic matters such as team structure, duration of the study and participation by client and design team representatives, as well as practical considerations such as dates for the study, accommodation, and the like. After the VMTC understands these major issues he may then draw up a list of *information* required from various parties for the study.

3.3   Selecting the Team Structure

The correct *team structure* is critical to the success of a VM study. When structuring a team one must be careful to strike a balance between the need for participants that represent various areas of expertise and a preference for maintaining an optimum team size.

Generally teams should contain between six and twelve full time participants to maintain optimum productivity. When teams increase beyond this magnitude there can be several negative consequences. First, the team can become relatively difficult to control. While some segments of the VM job plan, such as the creative phase, appear on the surface to be fairly free flowing, the VMTC often has to exercise control. This may merely be to orient the team down a more fruitful path of review or to avoid spending too much time discussing a particular issue. On these and many other occasions that would require control, the VMTC's task becomes considerably more difficult when the team swells beyond twelve members.

Secondly, large teams tend to inhibit some members and thus may hinder full team participation. There is an almost innate fear of public speaking in most of us. While a VMTC's role is to overcome this fear and intentionally involve all participants, this task also becomes more difficult with larger groups.

A tendency is for a few of the more confident team members to dominate discussions whilst more timid members become increasingly shy and less participative. As a key element of VM is to obtain multi-disciplinary perspectives, such domination of discussions is obviously harmful.

Finally, there is an intangible impact that is difficult to measure, but relates to team size. That impact is on team spirit and securing good rapport. It is somewhat easier for the motivating phenomenon of *'esprit de corps'* to blossom in a smaller team. This team spirit becomes a key ingredient of maintaining enthusiasm and thus *productivity* during the study.

On particularly large or complex projects, it may be advantageous to have more than twelve members. In this event, the problems described above can be mitigated by involving more than one VMTC and by splitting the team into a number of smaller groups. These smaller groups will work on their own with a dedicated VMTC for the majority of the study period, but will interact at crucial points during the VM process.

Within the practical limitations of size, each VM team is structured to suit a particular project. As it is unlikely that any two projects will be the same, due to the complex nature of construction, it is very important to assess the needs of each individual study when structuring the VM team.

As described previously, one of the key reasons for the success of VM is the concurrent multi-disciplinary involvement for a discrete period of time. Beyond the different design and construction disciplines, however, other roles may be equally essential. These other roles may include personnel responsible for maintenance of the completed project, user representatives and various experts.

Maintenance personnel often provide input from their practical experience that is not perceived by designers. An example of this was on a school construction project in a major city where the designers had included granite as a finish for a portion of the building's external facade. Here the maintenance representative pointed out that they often suffered from graffiti at schools and the common response by maintenance staff was to paint over it. To use granite in the location suggested would thus be a rather expensive waste.

User representatives can also play a very important role. In particular, they are able to assist the team to understand the operations that are to be conducted in or by a construction project. This understanding helps the team to focus on fertile areas for study. These members, often generate useful ideas even when they are not necessarily construction oriented. Sometimes people who are relatively naive about construction processes can come up with ideas that are not seen by the representatives of various disciplines as they are unhindered by preconceived notions of how something should be done. For such members it is all right to question most things without appearing stupid in front of the team.

In addition, *client representatives* often have valuable background knowledge that is not available to team members. This knowledge may spark useful proposals which would not otherwise have been considered. A good Case Example of this comes from a VM study on a zoo project.

Case Example

The zoo in question required that their animals be accommodated in exhibits which established an environment similar to their natural habitat. One exhibit in the project was required to show a predator/prey situation. To protect the prey there was a non-visible barrier between the two types of animals.

The proposed animals for the exhibit were pumas and mountain sheep. These animals come from a mountainous habitat and, thus, the design for the exhibit called for a large quantity of artificial rock which was very expensive.

The VM team included an executive level client representative who was, himself, a well recognized zoological expert. During the VM workshop this expert suggested that the animals in the predator/prey exhibit could be changed from pumas and mountain sheep to prairie dogs and coyotes. Since the latter's natural habitat is desert, the proposed change enabled sand to be exchanged for the expensive artificial rock. This generated significant cost savings. The proposal also had an added benefit in that the prairie dogs and coyotes were much livelier than the pumas and mountain sheep which provided a much more interesting exhibit.

Even on relatively straightforward projects it can also be very useful to include an *independent operations expert* on the team. Again, this member may be relatively naive about construction but may offer useful insight into the operations to be served which can result in ideas that would not have been derived from other construction related members alone. In the following Case Example, on a library project, an expert who actually ran a library was included in the team.

Case Example

This expert was a prominent consultant in that field. On this project considerable cost had been caused by a requirement to design the library to enable easy future expansion. However, the library operations expert was able to question this requirement on the basis of his knowledge of the impact of advances in information technology on future space requirements within libraries. He contended that in the future more and more information would be stored on and accessed from electronic media which required less space than the traditional 'hard' text of books and magazines. In addition, he envisaged that a growing number of future users would access library information externally using 'on-line' computer links and would thus not need to physically enter the library building. Both of these factors pointed towards a significant reduction in, if not elimination of, future expansion needs.

The various design disciplines comprise the core of the VM team. In the case of studies following the traditional route of using external VM teams the representatives of each of the disciplines should be of high calibre and be of at least equal professional standing with their peers on the project design team. Fairly senior staff are therefore preferred although these staff should be technically oriented and not managerial.

The actual design disciplines required will depend to a large extent on the nature of the project. Thus, for a building-type project a typical team, at minimum, would include an architect and structural, mechanical, and electrical engineers. Other project types would, however, require a different set of disciplines – a railway project, for example, would require civil, track, signals, and electrification engineers.

It is these core design discipline members who provide the predominant technical input into the study. While each represents a different field of expertise they are encouraged to participate in examining disciplines other than their own. This full participation produces a greater breadth of ideas from many different perspectives. It is not unusual for some of the best proposals to come from members on elements of the design outside their particular sphere of expertise. For example, when studying the infrastructure of a large research facility project, it was an electrical engineer who came up with the idea of reducing the originally designed two-way roadway to a one-way system.

In addition to the benefits of a broader set of perspectives, the fact that all the different disciplines are physically located together at the same time means that the implications of a decision by one discipline on another are immediately understood. Thus, if an architectural proposal is put forward there can be immediate identification of the corresponding mechanical, electrical or structural implications of that proposal from the members representing those disciplines.

Besides the design disciplines, various other construction disciplines may be included on the team. It is recommended that a *quantity surveyor* or *cost engineer* be included on the team to ensure the correct evaluation of the *cost consequences* of the various proposals. As will be explained in more detail later in the book, it is important for the cost estimates of proposals to be realistic and to consider all related cost issues. If the estimates are not correctly prepared, then decision makers may be misled. Even if the fault in the estimate is discovered during the review of the proposals and does not, therefore, induce an incorrect decision, its discovery will detract from confidence in other proposals.

Another construction discipline that is less commonly required on a VM team is a *construction manager*. Generally, the construction manager's input will be related largely to constructability and site operations issues, which may have significant impact on project costs.

The structure of the team will vary according to the timing of the VM study, as well as the project type and circumstances. Early VP studies may require different types of disciplinary input to later VE studies. There are several reasons for this. Perhaps the most important reason is that early VP studies tend to concentrate on broader, more strategic issues than later VE studies. Consequently, the team should have members with strategic expertise rather than technical expertise *per se*. Thus, when reviewing a retail project, a retail marketing consultant will be of more value during a VP study than a mechanical engineer, whereas during a later VE study the reverse might be the case.

Another reason is that the design of some elements, for example the mechanical systems in a building project, occurs somewhat later than the design of broad architectural elements. Whilst it would be worth having architectural input on broad issues relating to the design, there may be little for a mechanical engineer to productively contribute at such an early stage.

Finally, the team should always have a qualified *VMTC* to lead the team through the VM process and control the study. The VMTC plays many key roles. It is the VMTC who must fully understand both the tangible and intangible aspects of VM and who must apply this knowledge to direct the team towards optimum results. The roles and duties of the VMTC are described in the various chapters dealing with the job plan phases to which they relate.

The following Case Example describes the manner in which a VM team is structured.

Case Example

The following VM team was structured in connection with a project that comprised the foundations for a major railway station with a multi- building commercial overbuild.

- VMTC (a qualified Value Specialist)
- Geotechnical/Hydrotechnical engineer
- Civil engineer
- Structural engineer
- Railroad/Railway operations engineer
- Environmental expert
- Construction manager
- Estimator.

The commercial overbuild comprised over a quarter of a million square metres of hotel and office accommodation above the railway station. The site for the railway station was in a marshy location and was traversed by an existing railway line that had to continue operating during construction. The reasoning behind the selection of each of the team members was as follows:

- The VMTC was to provide the necessary team management and pre- and post-workshop organisation to ensure effective results
- As the project mainly entailed foundations work, a geotechnical engineer was needed; the particular engineer chosen for this role also had hydrotechnical engineering expertise; this added expertise was especially useful considering that marshy conditions were part of the site problems
- The civil engineer was included to provide expertise regarding aspects such as site development, site utilities and track design implications.
- A structural engineer was deemed necessary to analyse and evaluate the various loadings on the foundations caused by the buildings above
- As the railway traversing the site had to continue operating during construction a rail operations expert was added to review aspects such as safety, access, staging, disruption to railway operations, and so on
- An environmental expert was incorporated to identify and alert the team to any implications such as drainage displacement that might impact on the sensitive nature of the marshy environment

- Finally, a construction manager was included to provide advice regarding constructability issues and an estimator was needed to ensure realistic cost estimates of the various proposals that would result from the study.

The team was thus tailored to meet the very specific needs of the project. Various team structures pertinent to other project types are shown in Working Document 3.1. Working Document 3.1 is not intended to provide typical team structures for each project type, as each project's specific needs vary widely. It does, however, indicate how team structures change with both project types and stages of study.

Independent Team versus Original Design Team

General professional and industry guidelines in the USA suggest that VM studies should generally be conducted by VM teams which are comprised of members who are independent of the original design team. 'External' VM teams are considered advantageous for a number of reasons.

First, the use of external team members enables a fresh approach to a problem. The design of a construction project is a highly complex activity which needs the coordination of a huge amount of variables in order to meet the needs of a client within the parameters of applicable constraints. As a consequence of the complexity of construction there are a large number of potential design solutions available. However, once a design solution is selected that meets all the applicable constraints as well as clients' needs, there can be a subconscious switching off to further alternatives. Having obtained a good workable solution a designer may become subject to a natural human phenomenon that has been called 'single solution fixation' whereby it becomes extremely difficult to visualise further solutions to a design or problem. Such unconscious phenomena are further supported in the construction industry by the fact that designers are often faced with time restrictions due to both the pressures of fee competition as well as those of project programmes. As design progresses, the solution becomes more and more fixed in the designer's mind and each subsequent decision may be filtered so that it accords with earlier decisions.

When, however, an external designer reviews the design he is not encumbered by the same background thought processes and preconceptions and thus his fresh approach may result in *valuable alternative solutions*.

Secondly, there is the potential problem that original design team members may not be wholly *objective* when reviewing a design that they themselves have generated in the first place. Certain members may have preferences and biases in favour of particular solutions which will stop them from announcing or pursuing practical alternatives. Furthermore, there may be a reluctance to

Working Document 3.1   Typical team structures by project type and study timing

Library		Water Authority		Court	
Value Planning	**Value Engineering**	**Value Planning**	**Value Engineering**	**Value Planning**	**Value Engineering**
VMTC	VMTC	VMTC	VMTC	*Outside Members:*	VMTC
Library operations expert	Architect	Capital Accountant	Capital accountant	VMTC – Team 1	Asst. VMTC
Architect	Structural engineer	Process development engineer	Operations manager	Asst VMTC – Team 2	Court operations expert
Client representative	Mechanical engineer	Water quality specialist	Civil engineer (2)	Court operations expert	Architect
Mechanical/Electrical engineer	Electrical engineer	Operations manager	Mechanical engineer	Architect (2)	Mechanical engineer
Quantity surveyor	Quantity surveyor	Project manager	Electrical engineer	Estimator/Quantity surveyor	Electrical engineer
		Civil engineer	ICA engineer	*Client members:*	Structural engineer
		Mechanical/Electrical engineer	Quantity surveyor	Mayor's Office	Construction manager
				Mayor's Office of Construction	Security expert
				Public works	Estimator/Quantity surveyor
				VM project manager	

be seen to find fault with either their own, or their counterpart design team members', original design solutions.

Thirdly, external team members and design team members are likely to have differing strengths and weaknesses in different areas of their respective disciplines. Thus, the weaknesses of an original design team member in one area may be counterbalanced by the strengths of the external team member. In a similar vein to this concept is the notion that since the VM study is of a relatively short duration, the *very best can be afforded*, whereas to hire top designers for the whole design process may not be economically viable. Where top specialists are used during the VM study their role could be considered as that of quasi-consultants to the original design teams. Some VM programmes actually seek the best consultants in the world, so there may be occasions when consultants are actually brought in from overseas to participate in VM studies.

Finally, it may be difficult to get the original design team to participate fully in the process. The attitude is often one of 'well I know the project so why should I waste time getting to know it during the Information phase?'. This attitude often causes people to switch off and become destructive influences that upset the momentum of the process. It is critical to maintain the integrity of the process, even when the original design team is used. The reason for this is that various phases in the job plan force the team members outside their normal thought processes and cause them to view various aspects of the project from different angles. This, plus the fact that all disciplines and interested parties are available to each other during a study, always results in a greater *perception* of the project and often corrects misconceptions amongst even those members who claim to know all about it.

The main problem with independent VM teams is that an adversarial situation may arise. The original design team has spent much hard work coming up with a solution and can be aggravated by an independent team that reviews their designs for a short period of time and suggests improvements. This aggravation is especially pronounced when diluted versions of VM or cost reduction exercises are undertaken. With authentic VM, it is the VMTC's responsibility to communicate to the design team that it is not the intention of VM to denigrate the original design. It is rather VM's intention to work towards the same goal as the design team and to supplement their good work. In particular, the VMTC must assure that the team takes a professional stance and does not merely put forward proposals to 'score points' off the design team. Where obvious design omissions and errors are found during studies it is better to send a private 'professional courtesy' memo to the design team than to broadcast it by including reference to it in reports or communications with the client. The VM team must also be aware of the subjective nature of aesthetics and therefore avoid the natural inclination of traditional cost reduction exercises to immediately *downgrade aesthetic aspects*. Aesthetics are often an important function of a project and should be maintained where this is the case.

When authentic VM is applied, initial resistance by design teams is often overcome quickly as they become aware that the exercise is aimed at helping them and is not meant to abuse them.

When VM becomes pervasive, as it is in the USA, individual designers often find themselves serving on both the original design team and the VM team on successive projects. VM team members are therefore well aware of the design team's position, and vice versa. This increased understanding of each role serves to extinguish any remaining feelings of antipathy between the teams.

Despite the potential benefits of using external teams there is a tendency to utilise internal teams, comprising in-house staff and the design team, in the UK. While there are potential disadvantages to this approach there are advantages which may, on balance, outweigh them in certain circumstances.

First the potential for *adversarial resistance* to proposals is eliminated. Participation by all the parties to the project ensures that they buy into the proposals that are generated during the study. This 'buy in' greatly eases and speeds the process of proposal implementation (described in Chapter 9).

Secondly, involvement of an internal team in the VM study process has a major impact on *communication* between the various participants. This communication can uncover discrepancies between design team and client perceptions and lead to a greater understanding of each project participant's role. This understanding can play a positive role in team building which will benefit the project throughout its implementation.

Thirdly, the use of an internal team may be less *costly* in that design team members may be encouraged to participate in the VM studies as part of their original design commission. The cost of the study may be a determining factor for small projects in particular. It should be less important for larger projects, where the potential savings should swamp any costs associated with performing the study.

Thus the selection of external versus internal involves trade-offs which can only be appropriately determined on a study-by-study basis. A way of balancing the trade-off is to obtain some of the advantages of both approaches by compiling a *hybrid team*. Such a team would include internal members to obtain their buy-in and acheive team-building benefits as well as a number of external participants in order to introduce objectivity to the study. While there is a threat that the internal members will be able to intimidate the external members due to their superior knowledge of the project the use of a skillful facilitator should eliminate such intimidation.

3.4   Deciding on Study Duration

The study duration should be tailored according to the size, nature and complexity of the project, and in recognition of the stage at which the study is to be conducted.

The traditional norm for value engineering studies has been five days. Usually a five day workshop would commence on Monday and finish on Friday of the same week. This time period is sufficient for most projects, but additional time may be needed for very large or complex projects. Conversely, where the project is relatively small, say £5 million and below, a shorter duration may be applicable. It is, however, unlikely that an authentic VE study, during which all steps in the VM job plan are completed, could be undertaken in less than three days. Caution should be exercised in reducing study durations below this minimum as such a reduction is likely to impose limitations on some, or all, stages of the job plan, and such limitations could severely diminish the study results.

For VP studies at Outline proposals or early Scheme Design stage, similar durations as above would apply. For earlier strategic VP studies where the project strategy, objectives and requirements of the brief are under review, less time would probably be needed.

Most studies are conducted in one continuous duration. However, there may, on occasion, be advantages in splitting the study. For example, the study may have a break after Information phase, during which time the function analysis might be costed and/or additional required information sought. While splitting a study into two sections is unlikely to have negative consequences, dividing it into any more than that should be avoided, as this will hamper study momentum.

The study duration must thus be tailored according to the circumstances. Even though it may be tempting to condense some of the more arduous stages in the VM job plan, such as function analysis or the development stage, shortening the study duration below the minimum level needed to complete the job plan will significantly dilute study results. For VP studies at the Outline Proposals stage and beyond, and VE studies at more advanced stages of design, three days is likely to be the minimum. Earlier VP studies may possibly require lower minimum durations, depending on the project.

3.5 Determining Study Location and Conditions

The location and environment in which the study is conducted can have a significant impact on its success. It is very important to get people away from their normal workplaces for several reasons. First, if people are within their normal workplaces it is likely that the study will be plagued with interruptions as people attend to various day-to-day commitments such as answering telephone calls and various questions from colleagues and so on. Secondly, the mere act of physical separation from the workplace enables one to push normal distractions aside and focus completely on the task at hand. Both of these factors contribute to the level of momentum gained during the study, and thus affect the study results.

A common practice is to use an off-site meeting room which might be supplied by the client, the VM consultant or even one of the subconsultants on the VM team. When this is not possible, the usual solution is to use a conference room at a hotel.

The accommodation for the team should be sufficiently large for the whole team and a number of part time participants. There should be adequate desk space for drawings and access to various amenities such as telephones, facsimile machines, photocopiers, computers, and so on. Typically, flip charts will be required as well as various supplies such as marker pens, masking tape, blue tack, and the like. The room should have sufficient space to hang the flip chart sheets as they are completed during the function analysis and the creative phases of the study.

An experienced VMTC will often compile a 'box of goodies' to take to the VM studies. This box will be full of various small supplies, the absence of which can be most aggravating during a study.

3.6   Gathering Information

The quality and comprehensiveness of information upon which the VM study is performed obviously relates to the quality of resulting proposals. There will have been large amounts of effort expended by the design team prior to the study and it is up to the VMTC to gather the information gained from that effort in succinct formats that can be rapidly assimilated by the VM team.

Typical information such as the project brief, drawings, specifications, estimates, programmes, and design calculations should be, wherever possible, supplemented by information on site conditions, project constraints, and the like. A typical information gathering checklist is shown in Working Document 3.2.

This information must be sourced from the design team and client. It is important for the VMTC to build up an early rapport with the sources of information to ensure their cooperation. Once the information is gathered, certain key portions of it such as drawings and specifications may be distributed to VM team members for review prior to the study.

3.7   Site Visit

Site visits prior to the study can help the VM team visualise certain aspects of the project more easily, and thus assists in their understanding of the project. Even for greenfield sites, issues such as access, topography and site density can be clarified with a visit. On refurbishment or extension projects, site visits become more important and enable the team to better appreciate the existing structures. If the whole team cannot go, then at least the VMTC should

Working Document 3.2   Typical information gathering checklist

---

Project brief
Design criteria
Space programme
Construction programme/Phasing requirement
Drawings
 • Architectural
 • Structural
 • Mechanical
 • Electrical
 • Civil
Site plan
Cost estimate with backup
Design calculations
 • Structural
 • Mechanical
 • Electrical
 • Others
Specifications
Building Regulations used
Geotechnical/Soil reports
Environmental reports
Site photographs
Life cycle cost information
 • Discount rate
 • Fuel costs – electric, gas, oil, etc.
 • Project life span
 • Operations plan with costs
 • Maintenance plan with costs
Procurement strategy

---

make the visit. If even that is not possible, then site photographs should be provided.

3.8   Cost Estimate Verification

Costs are critical to many of the decisions made as a result of the VM study. It is important, therefore, that the cost estimates used for the study be as detailed and accurate as possible. Cost data from the estimate is initially used to determine those areas of the project which represent *poor value* and is used later to price proposals for *alternatives* to the original design.

Bearing in mind the importance of the cost data, it is quite common for the VM consultant to prepare an independent estimate during the Pre-study phase and then to reconcile this with an estimate prepared by the design team. Reconciliation will involve both parties' estimators reviewing any differences between their estimates and deciding which is more accurate on a case-by-case basis. This reconciliation often highlights misconceptions on both estimators' behalf which are then clarified and corrected prior to, or during, the study. When dual estimate preparation and reconciliation is not practical for economic or other reasons, then an estimate validation exercise may be undertaken. In this case, the VM consultant's estimator would review and check the estimate prepared by the design team's estimator for comprehensiveness and accuracy. This validation process will be less costly than the dual estimate exercise, but may be less effective.

It is not uncommon for neither reconciliation or validation exercises to be undertaken, but it is the authors' opinion that such activities should be a prerequisite to a study owing to the reliance placed on the cost data when making decisions.

3.9   Models and Comparative Efficiency Data

Various models are prepared and efficiency data calculated prior to the study. Both are intended to assist the team to focus very quickly on areas where *poor value* potentially exists. The information is displayed in formats that can be readily understood by construction professionals from all disciplines as well as lay people. This ensures that all team members are able to identify the most fertile areas for review. Models are generally broadly based so that reviewers are not bogged down in irrelevant detail.

Cost Models

A series of cost models that represent different cost allocations are commonly prepared in connection with VM work. Most are predominantly prepared in advance by the VMTC and cost engineers or quantity surveyors, and are then refined during the study. Others are prepared wholly within the study duration.

Cost models may be presented in two basic formats: *diagrammatic* and *graphic*. The format chosen is usually determined by the type of cost allocation being displayed, although both formats are often used for the same information. This is because each format can represent the same information in different ways, as will be seen from the various examples given below.

Figure 3.1 is an example of a diagrammatic-type cost model which was prepared on the basis of cost allocations to various spaces in a college classroom and laboratory building. The format allows a *hierarchical representation* of the areas.

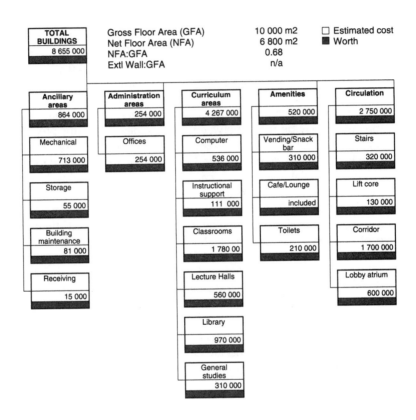

Figure 3.1   Diagrammatic cost model of spaces in a college classroom and laboratory building

Figure 3.2 shows the cost information from the diagrammatic model in a graphical format. The graph enables an immediate focus on the *high cost area* of corridors. Having quickly identified the main area of cost, one can then turn to a more detailed diagrammatic model or the cost estimate for further information. Costing by spatial area requires some degree of prorating of construction elements which are common to all areas. Thus the cost of foundations will be allocated on the basis of proportional areas and not just to ground floor spaces. Similarly, the cost of HVAC equipment will be allocated according to area usage rather than by its location within the mechanical room. While the prorating technique necessarily involves a degree of approximation, the models are only intended to focus attention on possible areas of poor value. Allocations do not, therefore, have to be exact but should portray the *approximate order of cost magnitude* of each area so that reasonable comparisons may be made between them. While cost plans prepared by a Quantity Surveyor for building projects, in particular, often portray cost information by area, they do not always do so to the extent required for full value assessment. Spatial cost models can therefore often 'raise eyebrows' when the various relative costs of different areas are highlighted.

Figure 3.3 shows an example of a diagrammatic cost model allocated by construction discipline and then by elements. This can assist the representative of each discipline to understand the costs relating to their area of expertise, while also sensitising the VMTC to the amount of time that should be spent on each discipline during idea generation in the Creative Phase.

Figure 3.4 shows elemental costs graphically. It identifies high cost elements and also provides an *elemental cost profile* which can be compared against those of previous projects to identify any anomalies.

As can be seen from the graphical examples, when costs are represented by bar charts, the cost elements are ranked by ascending or descending order to facilitate interpretation. Proportions are perhaps better displayed by pie charts, such as the one in Figure 3.5.

Besides the elemental and spatial breakdowns described above function cost models can be prepared. As these are dependent on prior function analysis they are not normally prepared until the study. Function cost models are therefore discussed in Chapter 4, which deals with the Information phase during which they are prepared.

Pareto's Law of Maldistribution

As described in Chapter 2, this theory of distribution can be applied to many circumstances and is used in VM to determine the relatively small amount of elements or functions that comprise 80% of the project cost. On the graphical cost model, a line is drawn at the split between 80% and 20% of the project cost to focus attention on those relatively few cost items that comprise the majority of overall cost on which the VM team should focus its efforts.

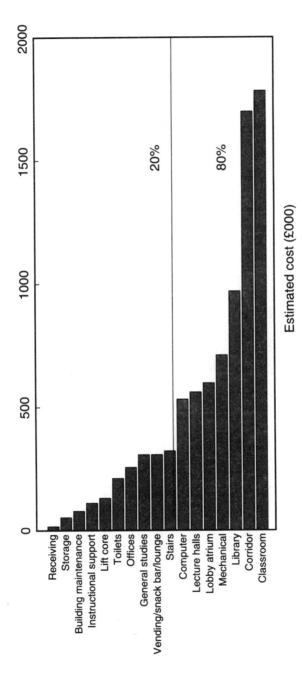

Figure 3.2 Graphical cost model of spaces in a college classroom and laboratory building

50

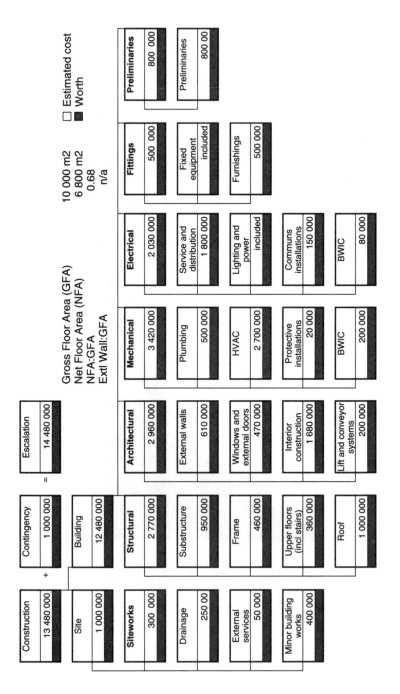

Figure 3.3   Diagrammatic cost model of a hospital

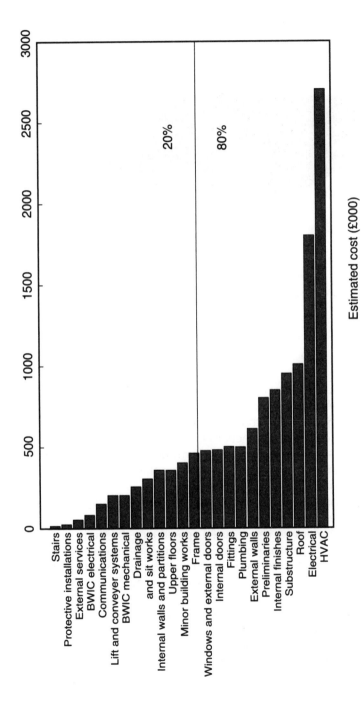

Figure 3.4   Graphical cost model of elements of a hospital

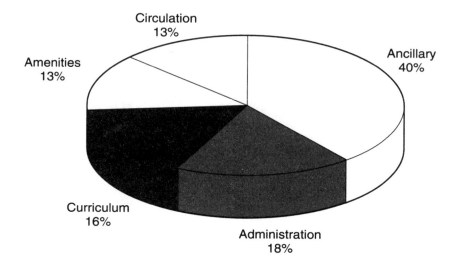

Figure 3.5   Pie chart of spaces in a college classroom and laboratory building

Worth

VM recognises that high cost areas may not necessarily be the best targets for value improvement. Whereas cost reduction exercises tend to focus purely on high cost areas, VM takes into consideration the difference between cost and worth of various elements or functions to determine where value improvements should be sought. The concept of 'worth' derives from function analysis and is thus considered further in Chapter 4 on the Information phase. The worth is theoretically derived from calculating the *lowest possible cost* of performing the same function as an item or element. Items with the greatest difference between cost and worth are therefore identified as the items with greatest *value disparities,* and are focused upon during the study.

While the preceding examples have dealt with initial project construction costs, models may also be provided to portray *costs in use,* such as operations or maintenance costs when sufficient information is available.

In conclusion, cost models are tailor made according to project type and the level of information required. While there are two basic formats, a high degree of variability can exist between the contents of different models. Their purpose is to facilitate the identification of high cost areas. When considered in conjunction with various other analyses such as function analysis and efficiency ratios (which are discussed subsequently) they can help highlight areas of poor value.

Spatial Analysis

In addition to preparing cost models it is often worthwhile to prepare a spatial analysis of a building project. The spatial analysis will comprise a comparison of the area measurements between the space required to be allocated to various areas in the client's brief against that actually allocated by the design. During the study, the VM may add a further allocation which represents the area they consider reasonable for the assigned space's function. Comparison of this analysis can reveal disparities between the design and the original brief as well as occasionally identifying anomalies within the initial brief allocations. *Redistribution* of spaces or the *elimination* of unnecessary space will improve the project. An example of an excerpt from a spatial analysis is shown in Working Document 3.3.

Comparative Efficiency Data

Certain ratios can assist in the evaluation of the efficiency of a project. When combined with the information from the cost models and function analysis they can help to determine *target areas* for study. Some of the ratios may be determined by the design team while others may have to be prepared by the VMTC. There are many possible efficiency ratios, but the three below are those that are used most frequently.

Net usable floor versus gross floor area

The net usable floor area represents those areas of a building that can be used for *profitable* purposes. It excludes those areas included within the gross floor area that represent support space such as circulation space in entrances, corridors, stairways, lift wells, as well as space used for housing mechanical and electrical equipment and the like.

The ratio is quite commonly used in the evaluation of commercial buildings such as commercial office buildings, but may also be used very effectively on many other building types. For example, on an educational facility studied, it was found that the percentage of net floor area to gross floor area was approximately 55%. The VM team considered that this was extremely low even for an educational building which required a high level of circulation space for a large volume of intermittent traffic between classes. Having agreed that a ratio of 65% would be more reasonable, the VM team focused attention on 'dead' space areas and discovered that most corridors could be marginally reduced in width without any detriment to traffic flow. It was also possible to eliminate some corridors through rearranging the building's layout. These changes resulted in a significant reduction in wasted space and produced corresponding savings.

Working Document 3.3   Excerpt from a spatial analysis of a library

Description	July 94 Brief (a) (m2)	Design (b) (m2)	VM team propose (c) (m2)	Difference (d) = ((c)−(b)) (m2)	Final Areas (e) (m2)	Comments
GROUND FLOOR						
Special purpose	18.59	21.56	0.00	−21.56		Eliminate unnecessary space
Lobby/Exhibits	158.92	106.69	106.69	0.00		Combine lobby and exhibit areas
Vestibule	13.48	17.84	0.00	−17.84		Keep revolving doors only, then no need for vestibule
Lobby	0.00	63.57	0.00	−63.57		Combine lobby and exhibit areas
Meeting room/Individual study	167.29	167.84	167.84	0.00		As Brief
Chair storage	0.00	6.88	9.29	2.41		Add projection room space to storage
Projection room	0.00	4.37	0.00	−4.37		Delete as unnecessary due to increasing video usage
Kitchen	0.00	5.20	1.67	−3.53		Reduce width of kitchen
Electrical room	0.00	10.50	0.00	−10.50		Add to telephone room
Telephone room	0.00	10.50	6.51	−3.99		Combine electrical room with telephone room
Lift machine room	0.00	8.74	8.74	0.00		As designed
Computer room	13.94	15.24	13.94	−1.30		As Brief
Elec. repair/Storage	23.23	22.21	15.00	−7.21		Minimum 3m x 5m; space allocation in brief excessive

Tech. office/Automation	12.08	13.01	12.08	−0.93	As Brief; move partition @ academic office
Academic office/Access	13.94	13.01	13.94	0.93	As Brief
Interlibrary loan	60.41	51.21	51.21	0.00	As designed; sufficient space for function
Storage I	0.00	1.86	0.00	−1.86	Include with space above
Supplies	13.94	15.43	13.94	−1.49	As Brief
Conference room	13.94	13.01	13.01	0.00	As designed
Circulation/Reserves work area	116.17	114.78	116.17	1.39	As Brief
Circulation/Reserves desk	139.41	156.13	139.41	−16.72	As Brief
Public on-line catalogue	27.88	27.32	18.59	−8.73	Reduced as space allocation in Brief excessive
Men's toilets	0.00	14.96	14.96	0.00	Missed from Brief
Women's toilets	0.00	14.96	14.96	0.00	Missed from Brief
Storage II	0.00	1.86	1.86	0.00	Missed from Brief
Photocopying	11.15	19.14	19.14	0.00	Increased programme
Word processing	18.59	22.58	18.59	−3.99	As Brief
Atrium/New books	4.65	14.31	14.31	0.00	As designed
Night Study/Patron Lounge	130.11	130.00	130.00	0.00	As designed
Subtotal	957.72	1084.71	921.85	(162.86)	0

External wall to gross floor area

This ratio is found by dividing the external wall area (which is measured over openings) by the gross floor area. The ratio is impacted predominantly by plan shape, the floor to floor or storey heights, and the overall plan size of the building. Comparison of the ratio of the project under study with those of previous projects may reveal anomalies that will then direct attention to the areas described above. For example, on the same educational facility described above, the external wall to floor ratio was found to be higher than expected. The plan was 'L' shaped, but this was considered to be reasonable so attention was then focused on the storey heights. These were found to be excessive and were subsequently reduced with a corresponding decrease of about 5% in the overall external wall area.

Gross floor area/unit

For certain projects it is worth analysing the space allocated per unit. For example, in a hospital one could compare space per bed, or for a school space per student could be reviewed. Such comparisons can also be made using cost as the parameter per unit. Thus, when reviewing an airport passenger terminal building, one might consider cost/passenger flow.

Many other ratios, such as cubic volume/floor area, etc. can be used from time to time depending on the nature and type of project under study. When considered along with cost models and the function analysis, they assist in the identification of areas of poor value on which attention should be focused.

4 Information Phase

4.1 Introduction

The primary aim of the Information phase is to get all members of the VM team to fully understand all of the major pertinent aspects of the project under study, and to get them to broaden their perspectives beyond their particular area of expertise. Another important aspect is to meld the individuals so that they act together as a team. In addition, the activities undertaken during this phase focus the team's attention on aspects of the project which represent the greatest opportunities for improving value.

4.2 Presentations

Being the initial stage of the formal workshop, the first activities to occur during the Information phase are normally introductory in nature. It is always a good idea for a senior management representative from the organisation for whom the study is being undertaken to provide a brief description of their goals for the study, and to reinforce their commitment to the application of the VM process. Such an opening gives the VM team an immediate sense of purpose and thus a good grounding for the rest of the study. Senior support of this type may also serve to suppress the disruptive influence of occasional members who are initially sceptical of the process they are about to undertake, and are reticent to commit their energies.

Following this introduction, it is generally advisable for the VMTC to provide a short address regarding the agenda for the study. This address may be supplemented with a brief description of the VM process if there are members of the team who have never been through the process before. While preferable, it is not necessary for team members to be experienced in VM. It is important that they get at least a rudimentary understanding of the VM process which is commencing so that they may focus their attention on relevant matters during the study rather than constantly worrying about what they are supposed to be doing. The overview provided by the VMTC at this stage will be supported with descriptions of activities at the commencement of each subsequent stage, as well as general coaching when required.

These introductory presentations will normally be followed by a description of objectives for the project by a client representative, and then by descriptions of the design by the various design disciplines. Each discipline involved should present their designs in turn. Thus, for a building-type project the architect may provide a presentation on architectural issues such as aesthetics, configuration, adjacencies, operational intent, and the like. This would then be followed by presentations by structural, mechanical and electrical engineers on their respective design elements. Where other specialist areas are important, such as security, brief presentations may also be sought from the expert consultants used for those areas.

The presentations should describe the current status of the design and provide a background of the reasoning behind the current design. This background should include full details regarding major constraints to the design and should identify, at least on a broad level, the various alternatives considered and rejected on the route to the current design. Upon completion of the presentations the VM team should have the opportunity to address questions to the various designers, in order to clarify any areas of misunderstanding.

As explained in Chapters 2 and 3 the VM team may be composed either of members from the project team or of independent individuals who have not had prior involvement in the project. When the team is predominantly composed of project team members there may be a temptation to cut the presentations short. This temptation should not, however, be yielded to. Whilst the designers may think they know all about the design, having been involved with creating it to that stage, they may only be fully conversant only with their particular area of the design. The process of providing verbal presentations often unearths areas of misconception between the various design disciplines which, if not addressed, would lead to poor value. Furthermore, there are likely to be other members on the VM team who have been less involved in the design, and the presentations will help them to understand it better so that they may participate as equivalent team members to the designers during the study.

The presentations should be followed by a quiet period for the review of drawings and other documentation by the various members of the VM team. The duration of this review will depend on how familiar the team already is with the documentation. While it is good practice for the team to review documentation prior to the study, this is not always possible. In this case, several hours may be needed for review following the presentations. Otherwise the review may only be of short duration and entail the checking of areas highlighted by the presentations.

4.3   Function Analysis

Function analysis is a key component of VM. It forces a broader and more comprehensive understanding of the project by stimulating intense discussion and by compelling team members to view aspects they might not normally have considered.

As discussed in Chapters 1 and 2, function analysis pushes team members beyond the routine initial question of what it is that is being reviewed to the further question of *why* it is that the item exists, i.e. what is its function? This additional question broadens the understanding of the issues, and opens up a wider array of potential alternatives.

Types of Function

The function of an item may be either a characteristic that makes the item work or one that makes it sell. Thus VM considers both sell or esteem functions such as aesthetics as well as work or use functions such as operational efficiency.

An intrinsic concept behind VM is that the process should retain all the necessary esteem and use functions. Unlike traditional cost reduction exercises, VM must be undertaken without compromising the quality, safety, reliability and attractiveness features the client wants.

VM thus recognises that aesthetics can be a required function to be retained. A question often faced, however, is the level and location of aesthetic functions required. A good Case Example which highlights the question of location of aesthetics required comes from the review of a government building in the Middle East.

Case Example

In this project, aesthetics were a highly important function as various dignitaries and VIPs frequented the building. When looking at the functions of various floor finishes, however, it was noted that a large expanse of marble floor was covered by huge ornate Arabian rugs. Upon investigation it was discovered that these rugs might only be taken up once a year for thorough cleaning, and thus the marble below did not contribute to a required function. Having recognised this, terrazzo was exchanged for the marble at significant savings.

Unlike cost reduction exercises, which tend to dilute aesthetics as they are the easiest target to cutting costs, VM seeks to maintain the level of aesthetic functions where they are required, or even to increase it if the required function is to be properly met.

Hierarchy of Functions

The functions of a project are arranged in a natural hierarchial sequence. The relative position that an item holds within the hierarchy is known as its *level of indenture*. The highest level of functions are those related to the broad requirements of the project itself, which are set by the owner's objectives. This level is related to the fundamental purpose, or purposes, for which the project is being constructed. Lower levels of indenture typically comprise areas of the project, construction elements and then construction components.

Function analysis should consider different levels of indenture to provide a broader understanding of the project. It is rarely necessary or beneficial to go to the component level during a VM study of a construction project unless an unusual feature is included whose function is not easily apparent. For example, it is apparent that the function of a building's superstructure is to support the building. On the other hand, the following Case Example demonstrates how function analysis is important with respect to unusual features.

Case Example

This example is derived from a story told to one of the authors by Bill Lenzer of VEI Incorporated, who has kindly authorised its inclusion here. The example pertains to a VM study undertaken to review the design for a large military communications facility.

During the VM workshop it was noted that there was a large, heavily reinforced planter which surrounded the building. The planter seemed to be overdesigned. Since the function analysis did not discover any special functions that might require the level of design which was shown, the VM team recommended a proposal which reduced the planter design specification to a level that they considered to be more reasonable.

During the presentation of proposals one of the attendees advised the VM team that the planter had been actually designed to withstand attack and was approximately 25 mm higher than the bumper on a Soviet tank. At that point the commanding officer for the military facility, who was also present, boomed 'What do you mean . . . a Soviet tank . . . on *my* base?!'

The proposal for the reduced planter specification was subsequently accepted.

Two Word Abridgement

For VM purposes, functions are defined by two words: a *verb* and a *noun*. This process is known as two word abridgement. The verb should be active and should describe what it is that the item does. It is often tempting to use a general verb such as *provide*, but this should be avoided wherever possible, as it may imply a solution. The noun should be *measurable* for use functions and should describe what it is that the verb description is acting upon. Whereas the verb answers the question 'what does it *do*?', the noun answers the question 'what does it do it to?' The noun should be *measurable* as it will be necessary to quantify it later to enable its valuation. The noun should also be broad in nature to widen the scope for alternatives. For esteem functions such as aesthetics *non-measurable nouns* may be used.

Inexperienced team members often find the description of functions in two words quite difficult and may be inclined to offer longer descriptions. The VMTC should, however, be reasonably strict about the two word abridgement rule as the approach offers a number of advantages. First, it forces conciseness, which ultimately saves time when people become familiar with the process. Secondly, it assures that functions are identified separately and are not combined with others so that each individual function becomes understood. Finally, the descriptions avoid focusing on specific solutions. This enables the team members to disassociate from the existing design, leaving them free to consider ranges of alternatives.

In addition, the difficulties involved in defining function with two words usually leads to considerable discussion which can at times become quite heated. This discussion is a vital part of the process of gaining an understanding of the perspectives of other team members, and should thus be welcomed. Rather than stopping discussion and moving on to the next function definition, the VMTC should encourage debate and allow the discussion to run its course within reason. It is often these discussions which unearth any *misconceptions* between team members.

Function Classification

Having established what the various functions are the next step is to classify them as either *basic* or *secondary*.

Basic functions are those which are essential and answer the question 'what *must* it do?'. On a project level function analysis, basic functions are those that satisfy the essential needs and requirements of the project client, but not those functions that represent *desires*. Thus, for a library project the function of 'store books' may be considered as basic, whereas the function of 'store cars' performed by a car park may not be.

On an elemental level function analysis, basic functions will be those features that are essential to the required *application* of the element. Thus for a roof covering the function of 'inhibit leakage' may be considered basic, whereas the function of reflective paint to 'protect membrane' is incidental and would not be basic.

There may be more than one basic function performed by a project or element. Thus, for a library located on an educational campus basic functions might include 'store books' as well as 'house students' for the purposes of studying, i.e. the library may be used as a place to access information or be purely used as a place to go and study. For an air conditioning system both 'cooling equipment' and 'cooling people' may be basic functions.

Secondary functions are features that are not essential and do not contribute to achieving a basic function. They describe what else is being done beyond the basic functions. In the previous example of the roof covering, therefore, the function of reflective paint to 'protect membrane' may be considered secondary. Similarly, in the example of the library, the function of 'store cars' may be considered secondary. Secondary functions commonly occur directly as a result of the method chosen to achieve a basic function. For example, reflective paint or gravel may be required for a bituminous roof covering but not for a rubberised roof membrane. Some secondary functions may be unavoidable, such as the functions of features required by Building Regulations. Where this is the case, the functions are classified in a third category of *'required secondary'*. During the Creative phase the VM team seeks alternatives that reduce or even eliminate secondary functions. Basic functions must be maintained; however, it is often alternatives to the manner in which basic functions are performed that yield the greatest improvements in value. The classification of functions as basic or secondary forces the team members to a deeper level of understanding of the project and its constituent parts. It also sensitises them to those functions which are essential to the project and must, therefore, be maintained. This eliminates the chance that alternatives will be proposed that are contrary to the project client's requirements and needs.

Deciding whether a function is basic or secondary can be difficult and is often very subjective. Different perspectives are drawn out when one team member believes a function is basic, while another believes it to be secondary. Again, such disagreements can propagate intense discussion which, as explained previously, should be allowed to run its course as much as possible. The VMTC should only step in when fruitful discussion has ceased or when time constraints necessitate interruption.

Cost to Worth

Having established the functions, they are then costed. Where a reasonably detailed estimate is available this activity will require a fairly straightforward process of abstraction of cost data. If an element or item performs several functions, the cost of that element or item may be *prorated* across the functions. While reasonable accuracy is desirable it is not necessary to be entirely precise in allocating costs to the functions. The main purpose of the exercise is to appreciate the relative costs of different functions and, thus, an order of magnitude level of pricing may be used.

In VM, consideration of cost alone is thought to be insufficient for the identification of areas of poor value. Just because an element or item has a high cost, it does not necessarily follow that it has a high potential for value improvement. Unlike cost reduction exercises, which tend to focus primarily on high cost areas, VM focuses on areas where costs are considered excessive by using the concept of a cost to worth relationship. Thus, where worth is significantly lower than cost, this is deemed to indicate an area of potential poor value that should be targeted. Theoretically, when this concept is applied to the function analysis the worth is considered to be the lowest cost at which only the basic and required functions can be achieved. The secondary functions which are not essential are allocated a worth of zero. Thus, in the example of the roof coverings, the roof membrane would be allocated a worth which would be based upon the lowest cost roof membrane available whilst the reflective paint would be allocated zero worth.

The worths are generally applied on the basis of the team's experience, and the amounts are only very approximate in nature. Having applied costs and worths to the various functions performed by an element or item, they are totalled. The total cost to worth ratio is then calculated to provide a *relative measure* of the value provided by that item or element relative to others. This measure is known as the *value index*, and a general rule applied is that when the index exceeds two poor value may exist.

The cost to worth concept may also be applied to the standard cost models which were prepared during the Pre-study phase. The worth will be derived from the least costly solution for a particular element or item. This worth may be allocated by the team from experience, or may be taken from historical cost analyses provided by the cost consultant or from published sources such as the Building Cost Information Service. Again, significant cost to worth differentials would highlight areas that may contain poor value.

Function Analysis Procedure and Examples

The technique of function analysis may be applied at varying levels of indenture in a large variety of ways. For building-type projects, function analysis may be applied on a broad project level whereby the functions of the overall project are examined, as shown in Working Document 4.1. The process may also be applied to the spatial layout or elements of a project, as shown in Working Documents 4.2 and 4.3 respectively. For process engineering-type projects function analysis may be performed on the individual stages of the process. The technique's use is flexible. The manner in which it is applied to a particular project will be determined by the VMTC, based on the nature of the project and the constraints of the study such as time, etc. Generally, the rule for function analysis is that it will start from the top and work down through the levels of indenture. Function analysis may therefore be performed on the overall project first, followed by spatial areas, elements and possibly even components.

Case Example

Working Document 4.3 shows a function analysis applied to two elements which were part of an infrastructure project. The infrastructure was to support several buildings, some of which existed and some of which were to be constructed as separate projects.

Working Document 4.1   Function analysis of overall project

PROJECT: CRIMINAL COURTHOUSE ADDITION		DATE: 1994			INFORMATION PHASE FUNCTION ANALYSIS	
ITEM: Total Project		FUNCTION: Enable trials			PAGE: 1 of 1	
ITEM NO.	DESCRIPTION	FUNCTION			COST £000	WORTH	COMMENTS
		Verb	Noun	Kind			
	New wing	Secure	Building	B	300	250	Staffing, TV, magnetometers
		Facilitate	Circulation	S	Included	0	Optimise movement of users
		Optimise	Operations	B	9500	8500	Facilitate ease of diverse activities
		Maintain	Parking	RS	1000	750	Project constraint
		Accommodate	Handicapped	RS	100	50	Required by law
		Minimise	Crowding	RS	1500	1250	Waiting areas, halls, lobbies
		Speed	Entry	S		0	Relative to security, processing, etc.
		Protect	Staff	RS	1000	1000	From the public and prisoners
		Separate	Users	B	1000	1000	No contact between jurors and public
		Coordinate	Operations	B	Included	0	Efficiently integrate diverse building functions
		Minimise	Noise	S	300	0	In courtrooms
		Facilitate	Transfer	RS	100	100	Prisoners in and out
		Control	Areas	B	1000	1000	
		Avoid	Hideouts	S	0	0	Lower order function
		Conserve	Energy	S	200	0	
		Temper	Environment	B	4000	4000	Heat, air conditioning
	TOTAL				20 000	17 900	Value Index 1.12

ACTION VERB
MEASURABLE NOUN

Kind { B = Basic
S = Secondary
RS = Required Secondary

(Basic Function Only)
Cost/Worth Ratio =

This Case Example provides a good description of how value indexes are calculated, and how the process identifies relative areas of potential for value improvement. Thus the cooling plant and distribution element, with a value index of seven, represents a more fertile element for study than the steam boilers and distribution, which had a value index of two. Working Document 4.3 also shows how function analysis identifies different value mismatches than might be identified under item oriented analysis.

Some of the buildings which the infrastructure served were to be capable of housing animals. In order that these animals were humanely accommodated, it was considered essential that the areas which housed them were air conditioned. The function of 'cool animals' was therefore considered to be basic. Due to the type of accommodation provided for the staff occupying the building and the temperate nature of the British climate it was considered that the function of 'cool people' was non-essential, and was thus secondary. Comparison of the costs for the functions, however, shows that more than six times the cost was being spent on the secondary function of 'cooling people' than was being spent on the basic function of 'cooling animals'.

This indicated a clear area of *value mismatch* which could then be addressed during the Creative phase. Another major influence on the overall value index for the element was derived from the cost and worth of the function of 'transport medium'. This function applied to transporting the cooling medium via pipework to the perimeters of the building served. Pipework within the buildings was allocated to the cost of the building projects and was therefore not a part of the infrastructure work. As the cooling equipment could be located within the buildings it was considered that the function of 'transport medium' was secondary and was thus allocated a worth of zero. While intuition might tell us that separate cooling equipment in each building would probably cost more than central equipment, the function analysis served to identify that this intuitive reasoning would be borne out only if distribution lengths were at reasonable levels. Thus, during the Creative phase it triggered the ideas of relocating the cooling equipment within the buildings or nearer to the buildings, with significant subsequent savings.

Advantages of Function Analysis

The individual steps undertaken during function analysis are often sources of frustration for uninitiated team members. This frustration is often most apparent in those members who have an engineering background steeped in logical processes. Function analysis is more of a forcing technique than a hard and logical process. Functions can be described in many different ways: there is no absolutely correct function analysis for a given project. Each of the various steps in the process are intended to force greater understanding,

Working Document 4.2   Function analysis of project spaces

PROJECT: NEW UNIVERSITY BUILDING AND ADDITION		DATE: 1994			INFORMATION PHASE FUNCTION ANALYSIS	
ITEM: Building units		FUNCTION: Add space			PAGE: 1 of 1	
ITEM NO.	DESCRIPTION	FUNCTION			COST £	WORTH £	COMMENTS
		Verb	Noun	Kind			
	Atrium	Set	Image	B	600 000	250 000	Improve first impression
		Afford	Interaction	S		0	Places where students may congregate
		Orient	User	S		0	Non-confusing circulation matters
		Exhibit	Art	S			
		Control	Access	B		10 000	Mainly at night
		Afford	Circulation	B		Included	
		Communicate	Visually	B		Included	Ease recognition of major building parts
	Subtotal				600 000	260 000	Value Index = 4.3
	Rear corridor	Minimise	Exits	B	40 000	5000	Single exit from all lecture halls
		Connect	Spaces	S		0	Easy access between elements
		Enclose	Route	S		0	Interior circulation
	Subtotal				40 000	5000	Value Index = 8
	Courtyard	Provide	Light	B	15 000	15 000	Natural light to outside
		Provide	View	B			Natural light to outside
		Permit	Socialisation	S	5000	0	Paving, seating, etc.
	Subtotal				20 000	15 000	Value Index = 1.3

ACTION VERB
MEASURABLE NOUN

Kind { B = Basic
S = Secondary
RS = Required Secondary

(Basic Function Only)
Cost/Worth Ratio = _____

Working Document 4.2   (cont.)

				INFORMATION PHASE FUNCTION ANALYSIS			
PROJECT: NEW UNIVERSITY BUILDING AND ADDITION			**DATE**: 1994			**PAGE**: 1 of 1	
ITEM: Building units			**FUNCTION**: Add space				
ITEM NO.	*DESCRIPTION*	*FUNCTION*		*COST £*	*WORTH £*	*COMMENTS*	
		Verb	**Noun**	**Kind**			
	Lecture halls	House	Users	B	500 000	500 000	
		Control	Sound	S	40 000	0	Soundproofing, etc.
		Control	Light	S	20 000	0	Permit type of lighting to vary
		Amplify	Sound	S	20 000	0	PA system
	Subtotal				**580 000**	**500 000**	**Value Index = 1.16**
	Switchroom	Centralise	Tele-communication	S	100 000	0	Primary control units
		Interconnect	Campuses	S			Computers
	Subtotal				**100 000**	**0**	**Review in Detail**

ACTION VERB
MEASURABLE NOUN   Kind { B = Basic
S = Secondary
RS = Required Secondary

(Basic Function Only) _____
Cost/Worth Ratio = _____

Working Document 4.3   Function analysis of project elements

		INFORMATION PHASE FUNCTION ANALYSIS					
PROJECT: INFRASTRUCTURE		**DATE**: 12 January, 1994					**PAGE**: 1 of 2
ITEM: Steam boilers and distribution		**FUNCTION**: Generate heat					
ITEM NO.	**DESCRIPTION**	**FUNCTION**			**COST £**	**WORTH £**	**COMMENTS**
		Verb	**Noun**	**Kind**			
01	Steam boilers and distribution	Heat	Buildings	B	580 000	500 000	Steam plant proportion
		Humidify	Buildings	S	190 000	0	Steam plant proportion
		Supply	Process	B	10 000	10 000	Steam plant proportion
		Discharge	Emissions	RS	195 000	100 000	Flues, low stack
		Meet	Regulations	RS	100 000	100 000	Tall stack
		Improve	Aesthetics	S	50 000	0	Stack cladding
		Provide	Resilience	S	185 000	0	Additional boiler
		Permit	Expansion	S	58 000	0	Future
		Upgrade	Ancillaries	B	63 000	60 000	Work to existing equipment
		Treat	Water	RS	35 000	35 000	Dosing
		Control	Boilers	B	140 000	100 000	Local control
		Enable	Installation	S	15 000	0	Demolition
		Transport	Steam	B	175 000	50 000	Pipework
		Transport	Condensate	B	55 000	30 000	Pipework
		Facilitate	Maintenance	S	100 000	0	Mezzanine floors, ladders, etc.
	TOTAL				1 951 000	985 000	Value Index ≈ 2

ACTION VERB
MEASURABLE NOUN

Kind $\begin{cases} B = Basic \\ S = Secondary \\ RS = Required\ Secondary \end{cases}$

(Basic Function Only)
Cost/Worth Ratio =

Working Document 4.3 (cont.)

PROJECT: INFRASTRUCTURE		INFORMATION PHASE FUNCTION ANALYSIS					
		DATE: 12 January, 1994				PAGE: 2 of 2	
ITEM: Cooling plant and distribution		FUNCTION: Generate cooling					
ITEM NO.	DESCRIPTION	FUNCTION			COST	WORTH	COMMENTS
		Verb	Noun	Kind			
02	Cooling plant and distribution	Cool	People	S	690 000	0	Chilling proportion
		Cool	Animals	B	113 000	113 000	Chilling proportion
		Cool	Process	B	30 000	30 000	Chilling proportion
		Control	Plant	B	45 000	35 000	Local control
		Power	Chillers	B	56 000	20 000	Power connection
		Facilitate	Maintenance	S	54 000	0	Hoists, ladders, etc.
		Transport	Medium	S	400 000	0	Pipework
	TOTAL				1 388 000	198 000	Value Index ≈ 7

ACTION VERB
MEASURABLE NOUN

Kind { B = Basic
S = Secondary
RS = Required Secondary

(Basic Function Only)
Cost/Worth Ratio = _____

derived from discussion and different ways of viewing a problem. The verb–noun description of functions forces team members to really get to the bottom of the question of what function is really being performed. It is often difficult to reach a verb–noun description, but the discussion it causes generates deeper understanding both of the subject of study and of the perspectives of different team members.

The classification of functions as basic or secondary not only sensitises team members to the relative importance of the various functions of the project, but also, when combined with the application of cost and worth amounts, helps to identify areas of poor value. While the allocation of worth is very approximate and imprecise, it forces team members to appreciate that opportunities for improving value do not necessarily lie only in the areas of high cost. As shown in the previous example, the function analysis approach can highlight value mismatches such as that of the cost of cooling people versus cooling animals that would be very unlikely to be discovered through an item oriented analysis. In addition, it is not uncommon that the process reveals items that perform no function whatsoever. A classic Case Example indicates this point.

Case Example

The Royal Artillery was giving a demonstration to some visiting Europeans on Salisbury Plain in the 1950s. Visitors were most impressed with the speed and precision of the light artillery crew, but one asked about the duty of the man who stood at attention throughout the demonstration.
'He's number six', the adjutant explained. 'I, too, can count. But why is he there?' 'That's his job. Number six stands at attention throughout.' 'But why then do you not have five?'
No one knew. It took a great deal of research through old training manuals, but finally they discovered his duty. He was the one who held the horses.[1]

Another Case Example illustrates how similar events even occur on construction projects.

Case Example

Upon deciding to construct a university building, the client elected to reuse a design for an identical building on another campus. A contractor was selected, given the old drawings of the existing building and the project was

---

1.   Jay, 'Management and the Machiavelli: A Review of Research Content and Research Design', *Academy of Management Review*, 1(2) (1976), p. 57.

constructed. After it was built someone asked why there was a wall several metres from the rear of the building. No one could answer until the drawings of the existing building upon which the new building design had been based, were examined. This examination revealed that the wall on the existing building was actually a retaining wall. The new building was, however, located on a level site that didn't need a retaining wall. The only function the wall served in the new building was that it inhibited access, so it was therefore demolished. Thus, unnecessary cost was added to the project not only by building the wall in the first place, but also by demolishing it.

Yet another Case Example shows how redundant operations can impact on maintenance work.

Case Example

During the 1980s problems were being observed with the concrete slabs in a number of New York City fire stations. The slabs were deteriorating due to the rusting of reinforcement bars. The cause was traced back to excessive water penetration of the slab due to it being washed down daily. After due investigation, it was discovered that the daily floor washing procedure dated back to the 1800s, when fire equipment was horse drawn.

Function analysis is thus a key component of VM. It should always be performed during a VM study. Where time constraints prohibit performing a full function analysis down to the elemental level, or the project is of a size and simplicity that doesn't warrant such a detailed analysis, project level, spatial and special feature function analyses should be performed at a minimum.

4.4   FAST diagramming

Introduction

FAST is an acronym for 'Function Analysis Systems Technique'. It was formulated by an American, Mr Charles W. Bythaway, in 1964 and first presented during the 1965 Society of American Value Engineers Conference. FAST leaves the verb–noun description of functions intact, but provides a diagrammatic representation of functions which displays their *hierarchy* and identifies logical *how–why* relationships. The diagram that results from FAST enables a broad perception of the various interactions of functions on a project. As with function analysis, there is no absolutely correct FAST diagram. FAST is rather a tool that forces us to place the various project functions in context. No two FAST diagrams are likely to be the same, even if prepared for the same project by different teams. It is, however, important that team members reach consensus about the resulting diagram for it to be considered valid. Charles Bythaway himself has been quoted as saying: 'FAST is a thinking process, you can throw the diagram away'.[1]

Diagramming Conventions

While there is in essence no 'correct' FAST diagram, there are conventions for its construction that should be adhered to. These conventions have evolved since the initial introduction of the technique to maximise its usefulness and provide an amount of commonality so that FAST diagrams may be understood by people who were not involved in their compilation.

A typical FAST diagram representing the various conventions described below is shown in Figure 4.1.

- *The scope of the problem under study* is delineated by vertical lines at the left and right of the diagram
- *Higher order functions* are placed to the left on the critical path, the highest order function which is the ultimate objective of the basic function is placed outside the left scope line
- *Lower order functions* are placed to the right on the critical path, the lowest order function is placed outside the right scope line
- *The basic function* which represents the purpose of the project under study is placed to the immediate right of the left scope line
- *Design objectives, criteria or specifications* which must be observed are placed above the basic function within dotted line boxes
- *The major critical path of functions* is that which runs centrally through the diagram from left to right; those functions which lie on the critical path must exist to achieve the basic function
  Other functions on the diagram may or may not have to exist to achieve the basic function and are subordinate to those on the critical path
- *Concurrent supporting functions* that occur at the same time or result from a function on the critical path are placed directly below the corresponding function on the critical path
- *Continuous supporting functions* that occur all the time are placed on the right of the diagram above the critical path.

Diagramming Procedure

The verb–noun descriptions produced during function analysis may be written on small cards or post-it labels. These cards or labels may be easily

---

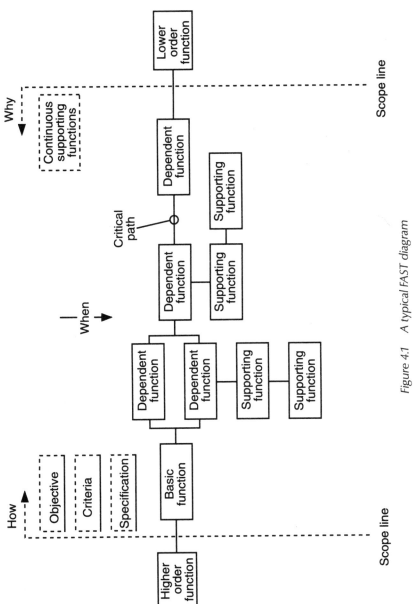

Figure 4.1   A typical FAST diagram

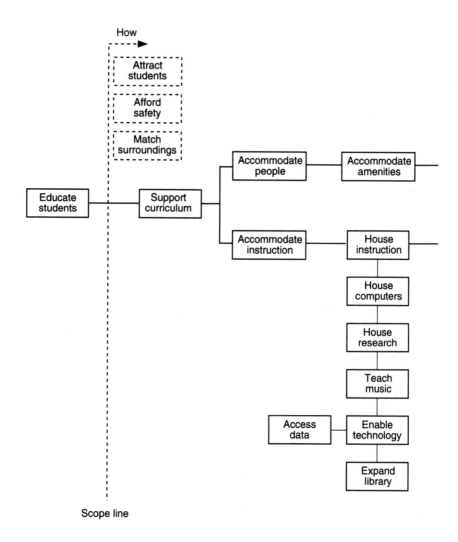

Figure 4.2   A FAST diagram for a college building project

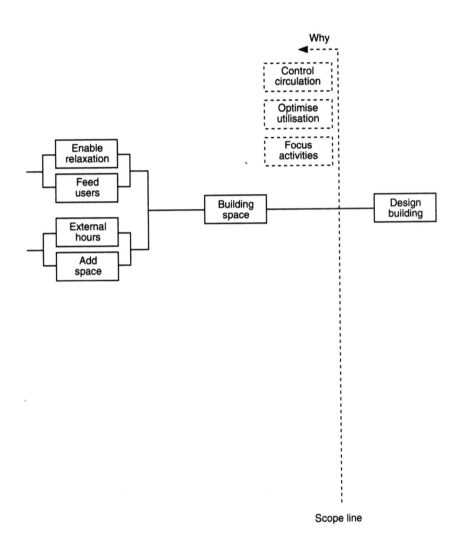

relocated as the development of the diagram continues. The diagram may be started anywhere by selecting a particular function and asking *how* and *why* questions about that function. It is normally easier to select a function that the team believes to be of a relatively high order and then to ask: How do I achieve this function described by the verb and noun? The answer should be supplied by one of the functions written on one of the remaining cards or labels. If it is not, another card or label may have to be written. Having listed several functions to the right of the initial selection by progressively asking how each function was achieved, the logic of the sequence can be tested by asking *why* functions are needed. These questions will start with lower order functions on the right and progress toward the left.

Often the initially prepared diagram will not totally agree with the how–why logic, perhaps because a function is missing or because a supporting function has been incorrectly located on the critical path. To finalise the diagram some iteration will therefore be required. It is best to be persistent and adhere to the logic of the FAST requirements as the full benefits of the process will not be realised when a partially completed diagram is all that results from the exercise.

Figure 4.2 shows a FAST diagram for a college building.

Benefits and Difficulties of FAST

One of the main benefits of FAST diagramming is that it enables an appreciation of the problem from a broad perspective, and allows quick appreciation of the fact that some lower level functions exist only because a higher level function caused them to come into being. Many times people devote attention to the *symptoms* rather than the real problems which *cause* the symptoms. Unless the real problem is solved, symptoms persist, no matter how much effort is applied to them. While certain symptoms may be dealt with, others often arise to replace them. FAST displays functions in a way that enables identification of the higher order problem, while recognising that dependent lower order functions are symptomatic of higher order decisions. Figure 4.2 thus permits the selection of the *right* solution for the *right* problem.

The FAST diagram can be useful during the Creative phase, when it can be used to prompt alternatives for how any particular function is achieved.

The principal purposes of the technique are to stimulate in depth thinking, to communicate the various levels of functions and aspects of the project in a broad and simply understood manner, to break the problem down into manageable portions and to identify 'real' problems rather than symptoms.

The usefulness of FAST on construction projects is arguable. It can be extremely useful in the very early phases of a project to examine a facility's fundamental purposes and its components. The usefulness on VE studies which are aimed at examining the means and methods of construction, is more arguable. FAST takes training and experience in order to apply it correctly. If the VMTC

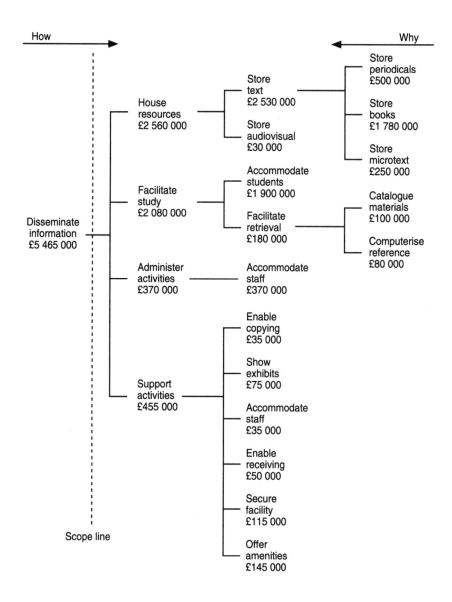

Figure 4.3 Function hierarchy model of a library

forces the use of the technique on an inexperienced team the process may become one of dictation by the VMTC. This will leave the team uninvolved and will thus not reap the benefits of FAST, whilst also probably frustrating and turning team members off VM.

FAST also takes time to do properly and completely. As time is often constrained during a VM study, there is a tendency to give up on partially completed FAST diagrams when difficulties are encountered. This will have team members wondering why they started in the first place.

Thus, while FAST can be an extremely effective tool which aids the VM study, a VMTC should use cautious discretion when deciding if, and how, the technique should be applied. When applied in the wrong circumstances, the VM study may become bogged down and lose valuable time.

Function Hierarchy Models

Another diagramming technique that follows the 'how–why' logic and can be used to display the hierarchial relationship of functions is that of Function Hierarchy Modelling. The Function Hierarchy Model is essentially a tree diagram which may follow how–why logic either vertically or horizontally, as in Figure 4.3. This model does not follow a number of the conventions of FAST diagramming such as identifying a critical path and is, therefore, often simpler to construct. When FAST is considered too complex for a particular project or team, the Function Hierarchy Model can be used to achieve some of its benefits. In addition, costs may be applied to the various functions at their different level to provide a very useful *function cost model*.

5 Creative Phase

5.1 Introduction

It is in the compelling zest of high adventure and of victory, and in creative action, that man finds his supreme joys.   (*Antoine de Saint-Exupéry*)

It is the Creative phase which is perhaps the most exhilarating stage in the VM process. When properly guided, the Creative phase provides a period of unbridled enthusiasm and intense productivity which can be an enlivening experience for all team members.

The aim during this phase is to compile an abundance of ideas regarding alternative ways to achieve the various functions highlighted and discovered during the information phase. First time participants in a VM study are pleasantly surprised when they learn how enjoyable and fruitful an experience it is. To a large extent this feeling is derived from the Creative phase of the VM study. Because of this typical reaction, it is the creative phase of a VM study which tends to make converts of those participants who were originally most sceptical.

5.2 Basic Principles of the Creative Phase

Creative Thinking Techniques

Creative thinking techniques, such as brainstorming and others described later in this chapter, are employed to push team members beyond their normal problem solving patterns towards *innovative* solutions.

Postponement of Judgement

Judgement of ideas put forward during this phase is strictly *prohibited*. Members must refrain from judging and censoring their own ideas, as well as refraining from commenting on those from others. The purpose of deferred judgement is twofold. First, by restricting comments, idea generation can occur spontaneously and without interruption. This leads to the production of a large quantity of ideas in a relatively short period of time. Secondly, and more importantly, judgement can deter the suggestion of seemingly unrealistic ideas. As will be explained subsequently, *unrealistic* ideas can prove invaluable in stimulating novel solutions.

Positive Environment

Whether you think you can or think you can't – you are right. (*Henry Ford*)

It is important to establish a positive attitude whereby people are convinced that their ideas will lead to positive improvements. Negative thinking and attitudes that thwart creativity should be consciously set aside. One should look for reasons why ideas *might work,* as opposed to the more natural inclination of coming up with reasons why an idea 'would never work'.

Large Quantity of Ideas

It is the *quantity* of ideas and not their quality that is most important at this stage. The ideas may serve either as a viable alternative to the current design or as a stimulator for further ideas. Some of the best proposals resulting from value management derive initially from an unrealistic idea that serves to shift thinking in different directions. It is usual for several hundred ideas to be put forward during this phase.

Hitchhiking of Ideas

Daring ideas are like chessmen moved forward; they may be beaten, but they may start a winning game.   (*Johann Wolfgang von Goethe*)

The importance of 'wild' and seemingly far-fetched ideas should not be underestimated. These can provide a base from which thinking can 'hitchhike' to valuable ideas which would not have been derived through normal thinking patterns. Indeed it is proposals prompted initially by these 'wild' ideas that often have the greatest impact of all the proposals generated from the study.

The process of hitchhiking of ideas is so rapid it is difficult to record the path of ideas that lead to new solutions. The process is somewhat akin to that which may occur during a joke telling session. If someone were asked at the outset to tell five clean jokes he would probably be hard pressed to think of more than one or two. However, after hearing other members of the group tell theirs, he remembers more and more. The end result is that he will usually remember far more than five.

5.3   Mental Processes in Creativity

Individual Creative Ability

Everyone possesses creative potential. It is difficult to measure an individual's capacity for creativity, but studies indicate that it is possible to improve one's level of creativity with practice and training. This creative potential may be evoked and improved by the *creative thinking techniques* described later.

General Mental Processes

There are three mental processes associated with creativity:

Imagination.

The opportunities of man are limited by only his imagination.
(Charles F. Kettering)

Imagination enables our minds to flow towards novel combinations of previous knowledge and ideas. While imagination may often be associated with children and daydreaming, it is a powerful process and requires effort and enthusiasm to invoke. Children have fertile imaginations, and they are very creative. But, since their creativity deals with ideas that are just unproductive fantasy, society teaches them to suppress their fantasies as they mature. Unfortunately this means that they also learn to suppress their creativity. This ability, however, is never completely lost; it just needs to be reawakened.

Another characteristic found in children that can occasionally enhance the creativity of solutions is that of innocence and 'not knowing something cannot be done'. This characteristic enables less technologically knowledgeable team members to lead the VM team to new ideas which would not have been brought up by the knowledgeable members. Professional and technical knowledge is such that we often subconsciously reject ideas because we 'know' from previous experience that they will not work. This reaction automatically closes a certain direction of thinking. An innocent team member may, however, propose an idea which opens up this closed direction of thinking so that a useful solution is ultimately generated.

Inspiration

Ninety percent of inspiration is perspiration.

While improbable 'wild' ideas may trigger thought processes and cause inspired novel ideas, such ideas normally only arise when you are already tuned into a particular topic.

Illumination

A creative thought will frequently occur when we are not consciously thinking of a topic. Such a process will only occur after prior deliberate thinking, however, and probably derives from the subconscious mind. This subconscious process may be harnessed by splitting the creative phase overnight, e.g. commencing on the afternoon of Day 1, taking a break for the night, and then concluding on the morning of Day 2. This procedure will enable team members to 'sleep on the problem', during which time their subconscious often prompts further fresh ideas.

Self-organising Nature of the Brain

Dr Edward de Bono, the distinguished inventor of 'lateral thinking', explains that the brain acts as a *self-organising mechanism*. This mechanism forms channels through which information is gathered and stored. These channels establish our normal patterns of thinking.

The analogy used by Dr de Bono is that of rain falling on a landscape. Rainfall gathers and forms streams, rivers and valleys. Once these have been formed, all future rainfall is channelled along these rivers and valleys. It is, therefore, the initial combination of rainfall and its impact on the landscape which determines the way that future rain is collected and organised.

This process is thus analogous with the manner in which incoming information follows preferred paths or patterns in the brain. The value of these patterns is that they allow us to recognise things. Once the pattern is triggered we follow along it and see things in terms of previous experience. The problem with this, in terms of creativity, is that the brain can only see what it is prepared to see and, therefore, analysis of data can only reveal ideas that we *already have*. The 'lateral thinking' techniques proposed by Dr de Bono jolt us out of our normal pattern of thinking, so that truly new ideas are possible.

This description of the processes of the brain also explains the manner in which seemingly 'wild' ideas provoke new ideas by prompting us away from our typical paths of thought.

5.4   Blocks to Creativity

The preceding brief explanation of the general mental processes associated with creativity provides a basis for understanding the *blocks to creativity* which must be overcome during this phase.

Such blocks may be defined in five categories.

Perceptual Blocks

Individuals perceive things in different ways. We often block out information which conflicts with our perceptions. A healthy aspect of the VM study is that it traditionally involves a multi-disciplinary group that uncovers the perspectives of each different discipline. Clients, architects, engineers, quantity surveyors and other parties, all see a project from their particular perspective which may be rather narrow. It is important for each discipline to be empathetic to other disciplines' perspectives so that all members get a better picture of the problem as a whole. A broader possible set of solutions arises from this greater appreciation of the problem.

Habitual Blocks

Any act often repeated soon forms a habit; and habit allowed steadily gains in strength. At first it may be but as a spider's web, easily broken through, but if not resisted it soon binds us with chains of steel. (*Tyron Edwards*)

Most of us are guilty to some degree of following procedures unquestionably just because we have always done things that way in the past. A good example of such practice is embodied in the tale of the civil service job created in 1803, which required a man to stand on the cliffs of Dover with a spyglass. He was supposed to ring a bell if he saw Napoleon coming. The job was abolished in 1945.[1]

In construction, such habitual blocks may derive from unchallenged standard specifications and briefs or habitual design practices.

Outdated specifications may occur due to a lack of up-to-date knowledge or from neglecting the regular review of repetitive specifications due to funding shortages or other reasons. Construction, like all industries, is impacted on by the growth in pace of technological change, and it is thus not always possible for designers and/or regulatory authorities to keep fully up to date with all advances occurring in some fields.

A Case Example of such an event was highlighted during a study on the refurbishment of an extremely large public swimming pool.

Case Example

Owing to updated health requirements, the capacity of the filtration system for the swimming pool had to be increased. The designer had proposed expanding the existing low rate filtration system to provide the additional capacity required. This expansion required a new building to house the additional equipment. A team member who was an expert in swimming pool design advised that there are now modern high rate filtration systems which had become the norm for new swimming pools. Utilisation of the high rate filtration system would render the new building for equipment un-

---

1. Alfred Knopf, *Up the Organisation: How to Stop the Corporation from Stifling People and Strangling Profits* (New York, 1970), p. 93.

necessary. This expert was able to produce the requisite backup document-ation to provide evidence that the modern system met health standards and the system was subsequently adopted. This proposal yielded savings of approximately £750 000, primarily due to the elimination of the need for a new building to house additional filtration plant. Moreover, the local author-ity's standard specifications were changed to allow the use of high rate fil-ters in other swimming pools under their jurisdiction, thus resulting in further savings on projects other than the one reviewed by the VM team.

Such circumstances should in no way be considered a reflection on the design team's expertise, as it is often building regulations that are unable to keep pace with technological advances. Keeping up to date with technology is a growing problem that is likely to increase rather than diminish for both designers and building regulatory bodies. It has been said that some 90% of scientists who have ever lived, live today. Such statistics indicate that the pace of technological change is likely to continue to escalate rather than to level off.

Another example of outdated specification arose when a VM study on an educational facility unearthed a requirement for expensive brass piping for water, as opposed to more commonly utilised and cheaper copper piping. In this case the educational authority knew that their specifications were out-dated but did not have sufficient funding to update them.

Habitual practice may occur on a broader level in a client's brief. This was evident in a VM study of the brief for a police station project in New York City, USA.

Case Example

The project was for a new police station for the 41st Precinct in the Bronx (known commonly from a movie as 'Fort Apache, the Bronx'). The original design brief followed accepted guidelines for police stations which required the building to have a basement and three storeys. During their review the VM team discovered that there was rock close to the surface throughout much of the site. The construction of a basement represented an expensive proposition, so the VM team questioned why it was standard practice to build police stations in the manner described. No satisfactory solution was discovered and thus the team proposed that the brief be revised to include a two storey building with a partial basement for mechanical and electrical equipment in an area where the rock was relatively deep. This solution re-duced the project cost by about 20% and pleased the end users in that the two storey design enabled distinct separation of public and non-public functions between the ground and first floors respectively, which improved security.

It is important for the VM team, therefore, to be free to broadly challenge aspects of a brief or design to discover suboptimal decisions made as a result more of habit than of objective evaluation.

Emotional Blocks

The greatest mistake a man can make is to be afraid of making one.

(Elbert Hubbard)

An upbringing of derision for mistakes and failure makes us all averse to putting forward ideas that may be suboptimal or incorrect. This aversion or fear suppresses the seedlings of ideas that may spawn new and valuable approaches. Members of the team should overcome their fear of making mistakes and put forward all their ideas, as well as countering and resisting temptations to deride the ideas of others. In addition, members must keep an 'open mind' and avoid overly defensive attitudes of any point of view, particularly during this phase.

Cultural and Environmental Blocks

The culture and environment in which we are raised impacts on our perceptions. A good example in the western hemisphere, in particular, is a general belief that analysis, reason and logic can ultimately overcome problems optimally. Research into the process of creativity, however, refutes such beliefs. In addition, cultural aspects can impose a strong desire for conformity which obviously stifles creativity.

Professional Blocks

Professional regulation and education tends to confine us within boundaries of behaviour and perception. While such boundaries are useful in certain contexts, their existence should be borne in mind so that they do not inhibit creative solutions.

5.5 Creative Thinking Techniques

There are numerous techniques available to stimulate creative thinking which may be applied during this phase. By far the most commonly used in VM has been *brainstorming*. Studies have, however, indicated that other techniques may gain better results on occasion. The techniques now described are not an exhaustive list of those available, but comprise the more common ones. While

the brainstorming approach would probably be optimal during initial involvement with VM, individuals may wish to progress to the use of other methods
described as they become more experienced. To avoid protracted explanations of these techniques they are included here with brief descriptions.
However, we have included a references section (in Appendix 2) for those
readers desiring more advanced instruction in the techniques.

Brainstorming

The members of the VM team are prompted to spontaneously produce ideas
regarding specific aspects or general areas of a project's conceptual basis or
design. The rules for brainstorming are as follows:

1   The problem under study should be described to the team *in advance*.
    This description normally occurs broadly during function analysis in the
    Information phase.
2   A *positive environment* should be established by the VMTC prior to em-
    barking on idea generation.
3   The group should be relatively *small* (e.g., up to eight members) and
    should consist of members from diverse backgrounds. This diversity is
    achieved by the multi-disciplinary nature of the VM team. It may also
    be beneficial to include team members from both sexes because it is
    widely held that their thought processes differ in some ways. In brain-
    storming, any such difference is an advantage.
4   *Illogical* ideas and freewheeling are encouraged.
5   *Quantity* and not quality of ideas are encouraged, on the premise that
    the more ideas that are generated the greater the likelihood of valuable
    ideas.
6   *Judgement* of ideas is prohibited.
7   The *combination* and *improvement* of ideas is encouraged. To enable this
    process, the ideas are written on flip charts for all team members to see as
    they are generated.

Adrenalin starts to flow in a brainstorming session. When individuals see
their ideas being listed as they present them, they feel encouraged to offer
even more; also, one team member's ideas will spark a related idea from a
fellow team member, and this in turn will spark an idea in another team
member, and so on. The idea in brainstorming is to keep these juices flowing.
Comments, particularly negative ones, during this process serve to act as a
damper. When a team member's ideas are shot down as soon as he offers
them, that team member will tend to become gun shy, and further ideas from
that source will be lost. A brainstorming session, when properly conducted,
becomes a fervent and exhilarating exercise for participants which generally
results in the generation of numerous useful suggestions.

The Gordon Technique

This is similar to brainstorming except that team members are not informed of the actual problem to be considered. Instead, the team leader defines only the general problem area. Thus in the case of a prison project one might discuss the 'ways things are enclosed' or for a multi-storey car park the topic for discussion may be for 'ways to store things with limited space availability'.

This general problem area is discussed until the team leader feels there has been sufficient dialogue. Then the specific problem is introduced and team members are encouraged to relate the points made during the general conversation to the problem at hand. This 'roundabout' procedure is used to avoid a tendency to derive habitual solutions when there is a specific description of the problem initially. The lack of a specific direction during general discussion can be frustrating for some team members but, with careful guidance from the team leader, the technique can yield innovative solutions.

Synectics

This technique is used to 'jolt' members out of their normal thinking patterns by using analogies and metaphors to describe a problem in an unusual manner.

1   *Personal analogy.* This is where you imagine yourself as *part of the element* that you are to consider, e.g 'I am a fire alarm system . . . what must I do?'
2   *Direct analogy.* This is where *similarities* between two items, functions, methods or ideas may be compared. Ideas from one application may be used for another, like the inventor who based the idea of artificial grass on the carpeting process.
3   *Fantasy analogy.* Under this technique *unhindered imagination* is sought. One might fantasise about an invisible boundary through which prisoners could not pass which would eliminate the need for highly secure enclosures. Such a fantasy should be followed to see whether it may lead to unusual but practical alternative solutions.

Lateral Thinking

Dr de Bono has developed a number of systematic techniques aimed at enhancing creativity. These can be used by individuals or groups to change the direction of thinking and, thus, introduce new ideas at will.

Only a selection of these techniques are included in this text, so readers who are interested in lateral thinking should obtain Dr de Bono's original texts for in depth coverage of his techniques.

Challenge

The simple process of challenging the factors that shape decisions in arriving at a design can have far-reaching consequences. de Bono suggests that the factors that impact our thinking should be purposefully spelled out and then challenged, even if those factors seem justified initially. He proposes that factors such as dominating concepts, assumptions, boundaries of feasibility, essential factors and others should each be identified and questioned. In VM on construction projects the challenge activity can occur at different levels, from broad concepts and assumptions to the choice of one design detail over another.

The huge potential for savings from simple challenge is portrayed by the following example of a combined sewer overflow project in New York City.

Case Example

The sewers in New York are designed to carry both sanitary waste and storm water. The water was required to be cleansed of both organic materials and infectious bacteria prior to subsequent drainage into natural waterways. The problem was, however, that treatment plants could only handle about twice the volume of sanitary sewage and thus when it rained their capacity was severely exceeded. This excess was discharged straight into the natural waterways without prior treatment. A number of projects had been under-taken prior to the subject project to mitigate this problem. These projects had all included facilities designed to contain the increased sewage volume caused by most storms and to disinfect those occasional overflows which would occur after more severe storms. Accordingly the subject project fol-lowed the same design guidelines. During the study it became apparent, however, that in this case the sewage underwent natural disinfection due to natural aeration during its journey. By the time the water reached the out-flow it was already disinfected to a level accepted by environmental regula-tions. Thus it was possible to eliminate the disinfection function. This reduced the project cost of some £500 million by almost 50%. Despite the fact that it initially seemed appropriate to use solutions that were appropri-ate on previous projects, challenging the disinfection requirement gener-ated huge savings.

Whilst the idea above came during a normal brainstorming session, the process of challenge is intuitively encouraged by VMTCs. For new practi-tioners, the more formal challenge techniques proposed by de Bono may prove valuable.

Provocation

Dr de Bono suggests that new ideas can be provoked either by chance, as in the story of Isaac Newton's enlightenment of the concept as to gravity when hit on the head with an apple, or by using systematic techniques. He describes several provocative methods, such as the escape method, in his books.

Under the escape method one describes all the obvious as well as hidden aspects that are taken for granted in connection with something, and then one must try to escape from them. It is generally taken for granted that libraries contain books, thus to escape from this supposition one could make the statement 'the library contains no books'. This could lead quickly to the idea that future libraries will rely more and more on electronic information and this would reduce future expansion requirements. Similarly one could use the provocation that 'a swimming pool has no water'. This could lead to the suggestion that a spray pool should be used for young children, as opposed to one full of water. This latter suggestion actually proved valuable in connection with one project, but was in that instance provoked through the use of function analysis.

Another provocative technique is that of the 'Stepping Stone' method which can achieve provocation in four ways:

1 *Reversal* of the usual way of doing things
2 *Purposeful exaggeration* of measurements and dimensions
3 *Distortion* of normal arrangements
4 *Wishful thinking.*

de Bono suggests preceding provocative statements with the prefix of 'po', to avoid confusion and wasting time in judging the statement.

A provocative technique that may be particularly useful when idea generation curtails is the *Random Input* method. de Bono suggests the compilation of a random list of 60 words. When ideas dry up one can look at the second hand of one's watch, or a clock, and pick the word which corresponds to the number to which the second hand points. Thus, if the second hand points to 25 one would use the 25th word of the list of random words, and then derive a connection between that word and the problem at hand.

The Concept Fan

This technique (from de Bono) may be particularly applicable during early VP studies when alternative means of achieving the proposed project's function may be explored.

To construct a concept fan, one moves from the objective of the creative session to broad concepts or 'directions' that may achieve the objective.

These broad concepts are followed back to more detailed concepts which are in turn followed back to ideas.

An example of a concept fan (compiled by the authors) for dealing with the shortage of available prison cells is shown in Figure 5.1.

There may actually be a number of layers of concepts between the direction and idea levels. The systematic construction of the concept fan forces the consideration of a greater number of alternatives than would be available from seeking alternatives directly.

Checklists

Some ideas crop up repeatedly in studies, and these can be recorded on a database which can be used as a checklist for future studies. These checklists may range from specific, with items such as 'reduced floor to floor height' or 'raise building out of rock', to more general, with items such as 'review space allocations'.

Care must be exercised when using checklists so that previous ideas are not force fitted to your problem, or project, in a manner which may provide *faulty conclusions*.

Attribute Listing Technique

By this method, the attributes of an element or function are listed in a detailed breakdown. Each of these attributes is then *questioned* and may be *modified* to improve it.

Crawford Slip Writing Technique

Team members are asked to write down their ideas relating to particular problems on slips of paper. There may be a number of different coloured slips of paper to relate to different problems considered. After a suitable time, the team leader collects the slips and lists the ideas so that the team members can all see them. Hitchhiking of ideas may then be encouraged in the manner used in the brainstorming technique.

This method can be a good way to stimulate teams that are reluctant at the beginning of brainstorming sessions.

Phillips 66 Buzz Session

This method is for use with large groups. The main group is divided into a number of subgroups in which individual team leaders are appointed. These subgroups then proceed with brainstorming in the manner described earlier in this chapter. From time to time the leader of each subgroup is requested to present the ideas that they have generated. The session leader may then redefine another problem or select one of the subgroup's ideas and instruct the various teams to generate more ideas on this redefined basis. The resulting numerous ideas are often diverse and valuable, and are produced within a short time scale.

5.6   Role of the VMTC

Guidance in Creative Thinking Techniques

The VMTC must *select* appropriate creative thinking techniques and provide team members with *guidance* in their application. This requires that the VMTC be thoroughly knowledgeable about the different techniques available, and the circumstances under which they should be applied. Often the VMTC must initially 'get the ball rolling', stimulating the team by proposing a few wild ideas or requesting ideas from individuals.

Team members will differ in their attitudes toward putting forward ideas in group situations, such as brainstorming. The VMTC should draw out ideas from 'shy' team members while carefully tempering the more enthusiastic members, so that the study benefits from each member's expertise and not just from the loudest or most forceful. Additionally, the VMTC must keep the study on track and bring the team back to focus if it starts drifting from the problem at hand.

Structuring the Process

Depending on the stage at which VM is applied, the process may be *structured* to consider initially overall project concepts, such as alternative ways to achieve the broad functions of the building or project, and then move on to more detailed areas. The more detailed areas may include operational and maintenance aspects and site, architectural, structural, mechanical, and electrical elements, which will all be considered in turn.

Recognition of Valuable Ideas

With experience, the VMTC should attain a level of *intuitive appreciation* of ideas with potential. When such ideas are encountered, the team should be guided to develop the idea to see where it may lead.

Deferring Judgement

A simple requirement such as getting the team members to defer judgement and commenting during idea generation can be surprisingly difficult. It is important that the VMTC gently, but firmly, stop comments or the session

92

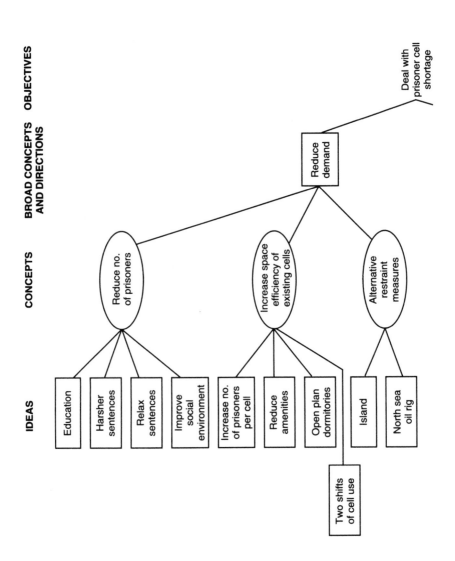

IDEAS   CONCEPTS   BROAD CONCEPTS AND DIRECTIONS   OBJECTIVES

Deal with prisoner cell shortage

Reduce demand

Reduce no. of prisoners

Increase space efficiency of existing cells

Alternative restraint measures

Education

Harsher sentences

Relax sentences

Improve social environment

Increase no. of prisoners per cell

Reduce amenities

Open plan dormitories

Island

North sea oil rig

Two shifts of cell use

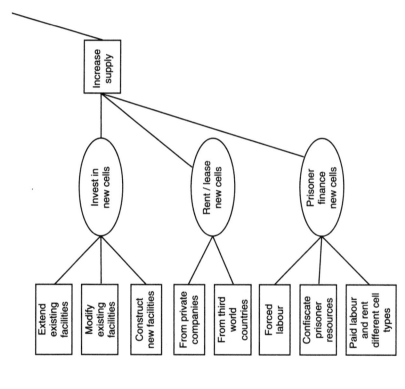

Figure 5.1   Concept fan for dealing with prison cell shortage

may degenerate into a disorganised babble which produces poor results. Each VMTC will develop their own ways to control team members. One effective device is to establish a 'sin tax', whereby members have to donate 10 pence or so to a kitty every time they make a comment. It also acts as a team building device because when someone 'sins', good natured 'ribbing' by the other team members usually occurs. This tends to lighten the atmosphere which is conducive to building *team spirit*.

Creating a Conducive Environment

The VMTC plays a key role in establishing a positive atmosphere, particularly during this phase. Members should be oriented towards looking for reasons as to why ideas *work*, or how they could be modified to become *valuable*.

It also helps if the VMTC can introduce an element of fun into the session, as this generally enhances motivation and relaxes team members, which helps to release them from inhibitions.

Recording

Either the VMTC or, on occasion, an assistant will write down the ideas as they are generated. These are normally written up on flip-chart pages which are then pinned up on the walls around the room as they are completed so that all the team members can see them. During a creative session it is often difficult to keep up with the speed with which ideas are being announced. Recording in this manner, thus inevitably slows down the process. In addition, comments may be missed and team members may stop actively listening to the ideas of others while holding on to a thought and waiting for the time to express it. Such occurrences may result in a loss of the stimulation potential of some ideas. While normal practice ignores such problems, a possible way to overcome some of them is to issue members with *idea sheets* which they each fill out themselves. These can be collected from time to time and given to a stenographer to type up on a computer during the study. At the end of the creative phase these typed idea lists may be printed out and used for subsequent evaluation. While such a procedure overcomes the potential problems associated with the flip chart method it tends to cause considerable repetition of ideas which must then be sifted during the evaluation phase. The choice of method is ultimately derived from the personal preferences of the VMTC or team members.

Ideas are generally formulated and recorded in *sections*. Thus, architectural ideas may be initially listed followed by mechanical, electrical, structural, site, operations and maintenance, and so on. An example of an abbreviated idea listing taken from flip charts on the wall is shown in Working Document 5.1.

Working Document 5.1   Example of a partial creative idea list

PROJECT: EXAMPLE		PAGE: 1 of 1
ITEM	*DESCRIPTION*	*RATING*
	ARCHITECTURAL	
A-1	Raise building out of rock	
A-5	Reduce floor to floor height	
A-13	Eliminate operable windows	
	HVAC	
H-1	Use ceiling as return air plenum	
H-13	Use standard filters in lieu of special filters called for in Brief	
H-17	Use deep well water for cooling	
	ELECTRICAL	
E-1	Eliminate emergency generator and use battery packs in selected fluorescent fixtures	
E-11	Locate switchgear and generator externally	
	SITE	
S-12	Delete parking	
S-17	Add bicycle racks	
S-18	Create smoking area	

5.7   Group versus Individual Creativity

One of the traditional arguments for the benefits of group brainstorming is that it provides synergy, i.e. the productivity of the group in total is higher than that of the sum of results of all the members if they had undergone idea generation individually. This argument has, however, been challenged by some studies which indicate that individual thinking consistently outperforms group brainstorming. Dr de Bono suggests that group brainstorming can waste time, suppress suggestions, and result in 'group think' – a phenomenon which induces suboptimal consensus. He recognises, however, that group activity may be better to develop an idea, particularly where different areas of expertise are required. This is the case in the review of construction projects. While it is productive to seek out and test other techniques, it must be noted that these other methods have not supplanted group brainstorming in VM as it is applied in the construction industry. In construction oriented VM, group brainstorming has proven its effectiveness in thousands of VM studies, and is still the universal norm.

While on most occasions the more usual group sessions are satisfactory for VM purposes, more advanced VM teams may wish to apply a combination of individual and group techniques to enhance productivity. The combined approach may gain from the production of a greater number of ideas during an initial session using individual creative methods such as the various lateral thinking techniques whilst also benefiting from the development and hitch-hiking aspects of group sessions in a second session. The combined approach would work best where team members have had some training in individual creative techniques, and would thus only really be suitable for experienced and advanced teams.

Individual creative thinking on its own would not be sufficient for VM, as the communicative advantages whereby each discipline gains from the perspectives of their counterpart disciplines would be lessened.

6 Evaluation Phase

6.1 Introduction

> Concentrating on the essentials . . . we will then be accomplishing the greatest possible results with the effort expended.
>
> *(Ted W. Engstrom and R. Alec MacKenzie)*

During this phase the desire for the judgement of ideas, which was suppressed during the creative phase, is released.

The ultimate objective of a VM study is to provide proposals which can be implemented. If the proposals are not implemented, then their potential value will not be realised no matter how good they were. It is important, therefore, to ensure that proposals are comprehensively thought out, supported with detailed calculations and are unambiguous. The development of each individual proposal is thus fairly time consuming. This means that the time limitations of the VM study limit the number of proposals which can be adequately developed. The objective of the evaluation phase is to screen the ideas generated during the creative phase, so that only the *best ideas* will be selected for development.

When reviewing the ideas, a conscious attempt is made to *combine* them where advantageous. On occasions, a combination of ideas can provide a more valuable solution than implementation of the ideas singularly, i.e. the total is greater than the sum of the parts. There are also circumstances where a combination will provide an effective solution from otherwise unworkable individual ideas.

Team members should be objective during their evaluation and consider both *advantages* and *disadvantages* of each idea. The positive attitude that should have been established in the creative phase should continue during the evaluation of ideas: ideas should not be discarded too easily. Instead, where disadvantages are identified, creativity should again be applied to see if they can be *overcome*.

A certain amount of sensitivity is needed during this phase. Although judgement is required, any criticism should be *constructive*. It has been said that criticism is one of the few things that people would rather give than receive. The VMTC should temper any members who become overly zealous in their criticism of ideas as other members may take insult, which will detract from team morale and hinder the remaining portion of the study. Humour is the VMTC's best ally in diffusing such destructive criticism.

At times, it is also necessary to exercise professional courtesy in the screening of ideas. Sometimes the team may identify missing elements of a design that are obviously needed and may have been omitted as a temporary oversight by the design team. Rather than highlighting such deficiencies to the client, the VMTC should exercise discretion and perhaps quietly notify the design team as an aside to the study. Such omissions are very likely to be discovered by the design team during design development, and there is nothing to be gained from embarrassing the design team by raising such issues publicly.

6.2   Procedure

Initially, the VMTC may prompt a discussion on the evaluation criteria to be applied during review of the ideas. While these criteria may differ with individual ideas it is useful to sensitise the team members to the broad criteria that should be considered as well as to their order of significance.

Following this discussion, the VMTC may read out each idea individually and invite the originator of that idea to briefly explain the idea to the remaining team members. The main advantages and disadvantages of each idea should be noted during this explanation. When considered appropriate, the VMTC will encourage team members to apply creativity to overcome or mitigate disadvantages.

After the team has listened to explanations of the ideas and discussed their broad advantages and disadvantages, an *evaluation technique* is applied to eliminate impractical ideas and determine the best ideas for development. There are several methods of evaluation available as described later in this chapter. By the end of the evaluation process the team may have whittled the original creative idea listing down by three quarters or more, leaving only the best ideas for further development.

Despite the information gathering activities undertaken during the Information phase, it is unlikely that an external VM team will be aware of all the constraints and considerations that will impact on the potential implementation of the VM proposals. It may, therefore, be beneficial at this stage to conduct a 'reality check', and contact the original design team representative or decision maker to review the ideas selected to discover whether there are any that are impractical in the light of considerations unknown to the VM team. A 'reality check' at this stage avoids wasting valuable time developing proposals that have no chance for implementation.

Once this final weeding process has been undertaken the remaining ideas are then allocated to individual team members for development. They are normally allocated according to the discipline affected by the idea. Ideas which impact on several disciplines, or which are general in nature, may be allocated to more than one team member.

6.3   Evaluation Criteria

The criteria against which ideas should be judged will differ according to each project and each idea reviewed.
Typical technical criteria may include, but not necessarily be limited to:

Cost

- Savings potential in terms of initial capital cost, operations and maintenance costs, staffing costs, etc.
- Ease of implementation and any associated abortive design or redesign costs
- Knock-on cost impacts.

Function

- Aesthetics
- Whether proposed alternative meets required functions
- Whether proposed alternative constitutes an improvement to the original design.
- Flexibility for future uses or expansion of the facility
- Safety during occupancy
- Security.

Time

- Impact on design time
- Impact on construction programme
- Impact on durability, reliability, and service lives of facility and/or its components.

General

- Constructability
- Safety during construction
- Jurisdictional considerations.

In addition to the technical criteria outlined above, consideration should also be given to political factors. If there are solutions which are strongly favoured by certain key decision makers then it may sometimes be futile to confront them with alternatives, no matter how objectively they have been thought out by the VM team. Developing such alternatives in the face of an obvious rejection would be a waste of precious development time.

6.4   Evaluation Techniques

There are a number of evaluation techniques available, each of which have strengths and weaknesses in particular circumstances. It is important for the VMTC to recognise such strengths and weaknesses so that the best technique for the prevailing circumstances can be selected. The more common techniques are described subsequently together with commentary regarding their effectiveness in different situations. The techniques are described under the categories of:

- Selection by VMTC
- Simple democratic
- Complex democratic

Selection of Ideas by VMTC

There are two broad approaches under which the VMTC may select the ideas for development, which may be defined as autocratic or benevolent autocratic.

Under the autocratic approach, the VMTC will select ideas for development without any input from team members. This process can be very fast and thus maximises the time for development. It also overcomes any difficulties that may occur due to the inexperience of the team. The major drawback, however, is that it fails to recognise the team members' knowledge and experience. The VMTC acts as a *facilitator*, and is not necessarily the best team member to judge the technical merits of ideas that were actually put forward by the team members who have detailed technical expertise. This approach, therefore, is not recommended.

Under the benevolent autocratic approach, the VMTC will select ideas for development, but will subsequently ask the team members if they agree with the selections. This is an improvement over the former technique in that the team members have a limited input into the selections in their editing role. The editing role may, however, still be suboptimal as the identification of all relevant criteria often only occurs after some investigative discussion. The speed that is achieved under this technique may thus be offset by the poorer quality of the ideas selected. As with the autocratic approach, this technique should only be applied when there are strict time constraints and when team members are insufficiently experienced.

Simple Democratic Selection

There are also two broad approaches under which a simple democratic selection process may be applied. These may be defined as consensus rating techniques and voting techniques.

Consensus Rating

Under consensus rating techniques, the team members are encouraged to discuss the ideas and to agree on an overall rating or score for the ideas, one by one. Several rating systems may be applied as described below:

- *Numerical 1–10:* This system is used to rank all the ideas on a scale of 1–10. Generally all those ideas with a rating of 9–10 will be developed into proposals, whilst those with a rating of 8 will only be developed if there is sufficient time. Ideas with scores of 7 and below will not be developed. Even though the ideas with ratings of 7 and below are not developed, they may be useful to a sophisticated VM client if future cost reductions are required. Upon recognising the need for further cost reductions the client can review the undeveloped ideas for potential savings in the order in which they were rated, i.e. review the ideas with a rating of 7 first followed by those with a 6 and so on. The disadvantage of this system is, however, that precious time may be wasted in discussing the relative scores of those ideas with ratings below 7. Team members might also be affronted when some of their ideas get very low scores.
- *Numerical 1–4:* This system is used to rate each idea with a score of 1–4, which represents the manner in which the idea is to be treated as follows:

  1 Idea is to be developed
  2 Idea is to be developed if there is sufficient time
  3 Idea has some merit but is not to be developed
  4 Idea has little merit and should not be considered.

The 1–4 rating system overcomes the major disadvantage of the 1–10 system in that time is not wasted discussing the relative ranking of ideas that are not to be developed anyway. It is thus a very effective system.

- *Dual rating system:* A dual rating system may be utilised which comprises an initial rating by technical and functional criteria followed by a secondary rating in terms of level of cost impact.

Initial technical rating:

1 Idea accepted
2 Idea accepted and to be developed if sufficient time and cost saving potential
3 Idea has some merit but is rejected
4 Idea has little merit and should not be considered.

Secondary cost impact rating:

1 High cost saving potential
2 Marginal cost saving potential

3   No cost saving potential
4   Additional cost.

Thus ideas scoring 1/1 or 1/2, 2/1 and so on will be developed as the best ideas which combine technical and cost improvement. Problems associated with this system are that it is more complicated than the single rating systems and thus may be more time consuming. In addition, it tends to eliminate very good technical ideas that result in some additional cost even though they may represent good value.

- *Accept/Reject system:*   This is the simplest rating technique, whereby ideas are either simply accepted or rejected. Whilst this seems a simpler approach than the others it can, in fact, be time consuming in that there are no compromises or middle positions. This means that members tend to argue more fervently for an acceptance or rejection. In addition, the system fails to provide the client with a relative scoring of ideas which were not developed which, as previously discussed, may be useful for later cost reduction exercises.

One of the major advantages of the consensus rating techniques is that they enable investigative discussion of the ideas, and thus the ideas selected have the benefit of expert technical consideration in their selection. Open discussion can, however, be difficult to control, particularly for an inexperienced VMTC. A careful balance must be struck between the need for sufficient discussion and wasting precious development time in discussing ideas for too long. In addition, the VMTC must encourage relatively equal participation by team members so that no one member dominates the discussions and thus biases the selection process.

Voting

Voting for ideas may occur with or without discussion by team members. The former approach involves the two steps of team members voting for ideas which they believe have merit and then deciding on the number of votes needed for an idea to be developed. The latter approach adds a third step of discussion of the ideas selected during voting.

An equal number of votes is awarded to each team member and that number is generally limited to half or less of the number of ideas generated during the creative phase. It is important that each member is allowed to cast only one vote for any individual idea, and that members vote independently from each other for the ideas that are best from all disciplines and not just their own.

One practical method to limit the number of votes and avoid multiple voting is to issue each team member a set number of sticky labels which they each initial. Team members may then stick one label against each of their favoured ideas which will generally be listed on the pages of a flip chart which have been pinned up around the room.

Once the votes have been allocated, they may be collated and totalled for each idea. Then the team or VMTC can decide how many votes are necessary in order for an idea to be developed.

This method of voting is very quick and involves all of the team members. However, if discussion of the ideas selected is not allowed there is a major drawback in that some ideas which are non viable due to technical or cost implications may actually receive enough votes for them to be developed. The reason for this is that votes are cast by team members for all disciplines and not just their own. Individuals may thus vote for ideas without a full appreciation of the implications of those ideas beyond their domain of expertise. Consequently, this method is flawed and is not recommended by the authors. However, for this reason voting with subsequent discussion is frequently used so that the experts in the various disciplines may object and highlight any ideas that have been voted as favourable but, in reality, are impractical for reasons not initially understood by those voting for them. This is a viable method.

Voting methods are quick and do not require a large degree of control from the VMTC.

Complex Democratic

The techniques categorised under this title consist of techniques that first weigh evaluation criteria according to their relative importance and then score alternatives on the basis of the weighted criteria to determine those that are optimal. The technique discussed here is that of the combined Criteria Scoring Matrix and Alternative Analysis Matrix.

The process involved with the Combined Scoring Matrix and Alternative Analysis is indicated in Figure 6.1 and is detailed in the following text:

Step 1: Select the criteria and list them on the left hand side of the Criteria Scoring Matrix. While there is theoretically no limit on the number of criteria used it is rare in a VM study to allocate more than twenty, due to time constraints. Generally the number of criteria will range from 5–10. As shown in Figure 6.1, each criterion corresponds to a letter, e.g. initial cost is *A*, aesthetics is *B*, and so on. The reason for this will become clear during the later steps.

It is very important that each criteria is wholly independent of the others because any overlaps will skew or bias the results. A common error is to include both initial costs and total life cycle costs as separate criteria. As initial cost forms a portion of the total life cycle cost the inclusion of both as

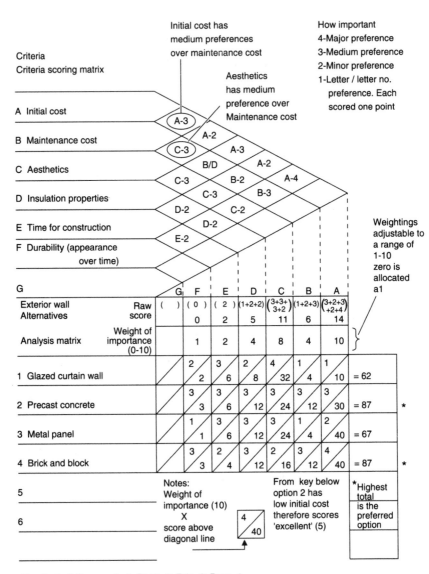

Excellent - 5; Very good - 4; Good - 3; Fair - 2; Poor - 1

Source: based on A. J. Dell'Isola and S. J. Kirk, *Life Cycle Costing for Design Professionals* (McGraw-Hill, 1981).

Figure 6.1   Evaluation of external wall alternatives using combined scoring matrix and alternative analysis

separate criteria would mean that initial costs is in effect included twice and is, therefore, allocated excessive weighting. One must also guard against taking one issue and including it as a number of criteria.

Step 2: Having established the criteria, the next step is to assign a relative weight of importance to each of them. Whilst this could be achieved subjectively by allocating weightings based on team members' intuition, the Criteria Scoring Matrix enables an objective analysis. This objective analysis commences with the comparison and rating of each criteria against all of the others. Thus criterion *A* will be compared against criteria *B*, then *C*, then *D*, and so on. During comparison it is decided which of the two criteria is more important, and the more important criteria is rated according to the following key:

4   Major preference over other criteria
3   Medium preference over other criteria
2   Minor preference over other criteria
1   No preference over other criteria.

The more important criterion, together with its score from the above key, is then written into the box where the two criteria intersect on the matrix. Thus, on Figure 6.1 you would start in the top left hand corner of the matrix by comparing criterion *A* to criterion *B*. Figure 6.1 indicates that it was decided that *A* had a medium preference over *B* and thus 'A–3' was written in the box where *A* and *B* intersect on the matrix. When compared against criterion *C*, *A* was again considered more important, but had only a minor preference, on this occasion, and so 'A–2' was written in the intersecting box. This process is repeated until each criterion has been compared against all of the other various criteria.

Step 3: Once the comparisons have been completed, the scores for each letter may be totalled to provide a relative weighting for each of the criteria. This totalling provides the 'raw score' indicated at the bottom of the Criteria Scoring Matrix. While these raw scores can be used as the weightings for each of the criteria it is often more easy to understand and appreciate the relative weightings if they are converted from the raw score to a weighting score range from 1 to 10. Thus the highest raw score will be allocated a weighting of 10 and lower raw score, will be allocated a pro rated score between 1 and 10. If any criteria have a raw score of zero they are assigned a minimum weighting of 1 so that they are not eliminated totally from consideration during the comparison of alternatives.

Step 4: Having assigned weightings to each of the criteria one then moves to *comparison* of the various design solution alternatives on the Alternatives Analysis Matrix. Here the first step is to evaluate each alternative in turn against each of the criteria. This evaluation consists of reviewing the alternative against a criterion and scoring it according to the following key:

5   Excellent
4   Very good
3   Good
2   Fair
1   Poor.

The score is inserted below the diagonal line in the box which represents the matrix intersection between the alternative and criteria. Thus, in Figure 6.1 where alternative 1 is evaluated in terms of criterion *A* (initial cost) the alternative is allocated a score of only 1 (poor), as it is considered that the proposed design solution is relatively expensive.

Step 5:   The next step is to convert the scores of the alternatives against criteria to *weighted* scores which reflect the varying degrees of importance of each of the criteria. This is achieved by multiplying the weight of importance for the criteria (at the top of the matrix) against the score achieved by the alternative (below diagonal of box where alternatives and criteria intersect). The result of this multiplication is inserted above the diagonal line in the box which represents the matrix intersection between the alternative and criteria. In Figure 6.1, therefore, the weighted score of alternative 1 in respect of criterion *A* becomes 10 which derives from a score of 1 multiplied by a weighting of 10.

Step 6:   The final step is to total the weighted scores for each of the alternatives in the total column on the right hand side of the Alternatives Analysis Matrix. The alternative with the highest score is then taken to be the *optimal solution,* and should be selected. Often several of the alternatives achieve fairly similar scores in which case there may be more than one alternative that is selected for development.

This evaluation approach can be seen to be far more sophisticated than the previous approaches. While it takes greater effort and time, the technique is very useful when considering complicated situations or when it is important that the final decision maker(s) understand(s) the manner in which alternatives were selected. The approach enables the objective consideration of numerous criteria consisting of both economic and non- economic factors.

The technique may be applied on the micro scale to evaluate alternatives for project elements or components as shown in Working Document 6.1 and Figure 6.1. It may also be very effectively applied on a macro scale either to assess alternative schemes or project designs during feasibility stage or to rank and select optimal projects for a multiple project construction programme with limited resources.

While this approach does produce an optimal solution it may be felt that this solution is unwarranted once the final outcome is totalled. Iteration is thus required to reach a reasonable answer using this technique. Perhaps the major benefit of the technique is gained not from quantitatively calculating

Working Document 6.1   Guidelines for selection of an evaluation technique

CIRCUMSTANCE\TECHNIQUE		SELECTION BY VMTC		SIMPLE DEMOCRATIC			COMPLEX DEMOCRATIC
		AUTOCRATIC	BENEVOLENT AUTOCRATIC	RANKING BY CONSENSUS	VOTING — Without discussion	VOTING — With discussion	CRITERIA SCORING MATRIX
STUDY DURATION	Very short						
	Short	N			N		
	Medium	O	X	X	O		
	Long	T		X	T	X	X
PERSONALITY OF VMTC	Autocratic	R	X		R		
	Benevolent autocratic	E	X	X	E	X	
	Democratic	C		X	C	X	X
	Strong	O		X	O	X	X
PROJECT ISSUE COMPLEXITY	Low	M	X		M		
	Average	M	X	X	M	X	X
	High	E		X	E	X	X
PROJECT STAGE	Briefing	N		X	D	X	
	Sketch plans	D	X	X	E	X	X
	Detail design	E	X	X	D	X	X
LEVEL OF DECISION DOCUMENTATION REQUIRED	Low	D	X				
	Moderate			X	X	X	X
	High			X		X	X

the 'best' solution, but is derived from being forced to review all the pertinent criteria in an objective manner.

6.5   Repeating the Evaluation Procedure

Quite often the initial rating of ideas fails to reduce the number to be developed to a realistic level. If this happens, the team should run through the ideas highlighted for development to see which should be retained and which can be deferred for development if sufficient time is available. The actual number of ideas that can be reasonably developed will depend on the level of detail required for the proposals, the duration of the study, the team size, and several other factors. The number of ideas which should be developed is thus generally established by the VMTC based on experience and an appreciation of the various circumstances of the study.

7 Development Phase

7.1 Introduction

The goal of this phase is to develop the ideas selected during the preceding Evaluation phase into practicable proposals. This is perhaps the most laborious phase in the VM job plan, but is also critically important.

The Development phase is where the technical expertise of the members of the team becomes essential. The ideas proposed must be researched and translated into proposed alternative designs, supported by backup calculations, sketches and descriptions of cost and other implications. The work involved in these activities causes this phase to be the most time consuming of the five job plan phases. It normally constitutes well over half of the time needed to conduct a study workshop, and this factor should be borne in mind when establishing the study agenda.

While some ideas may be combined to form one proposal, each proposal developed should be treated separately. It is common to have *mutually exclusive proposals*, whereby if one proposal is selected its selection will preclude the adoption of another proposal. This occurs when the team proposes a number of alternatives to one particular design aspect.

Site Example

In a recent study there were two alternatives considered against an original design of exterior granite pavers. These two alternatives were written up as separate proposals for alternative pavers of patterned concrete or terrazzo. The proposal of alternative finishes was motivated by the fact that the granite pavers would prove to be a maintenance problem rather than purely because of their high cost. By giving two proposals which were aesthetically responsible the design team were given a level of choice between proposals.

In situations such as this where there are important aesthetic considerations, it is helpful to provide a number of lower cost options. A singular proposal may be relatively easy to reject whereas rejection of all either/or proposals will be unlikely.

Being one of the arduous and time consuming phases of the job plan, there may be temptations to abbreviate the activities of the Development Phase. Inexperienced users of VM may yield to this temptation without realising the serious consequences of diluting the development process. It is the opinion of the authors that comprehensive development of proposals is a critical aspect of a VM study, especially when external teams are used.

The importance of developing comprehensive proposals derives from a number of factors. First, a detailed level of development provides an extension to the evaluation process. The processes involved in the Evaluation phase are intended to select a reasonable number of the best ideas generated during the Creative phase which are then developed into proposals during the Development phase. The review is thus relatively cursory in nature. While considering potential economic and non-economic advantages and disadvantages of ideas in selecting ideas for development, the Evaluation phase can only elect ideas to pursue based on team members' first judgement of the potential of those ideas, without the benefit of complete analysis.

The potential of these ideas is tested during development when design calculations such as structural loadings, etc. and design sketches are prepared. It is not uncommon for these calculations and in depth consideration of the implications of the idea to negate the perceived benefits of the idea. When this is discovered, the proposal is dropped and will obviously not be recommended for consideration.

Without the detailed development activities such unworkable proposals may actually be recommended. When due investigation by the design team discovers the proposal to be unworkable it will raise in their minds the question of credibility of remaining proposals and quite naturally orient them toward a defensive stature. Moreover, suggesting unworkable proposals disrupts the design process and can waste the design team's time. Such disruptions cannot be afforded within increasingly constrained design programmes.

Secondly, if descriptions of proposals are not detailed and supported with backup data they may not be understood correctly by decision makers. This miscommunication may cause a proposal to be rejected even when it was in reality a workable and beneficial proposal.

Thirdly, when external teams are used the development of detailed proposals minimises any disruption to the design programme. The VM team should be empathetic to the design team's position when developing proposals. Sufficient detail is needed for the design team to be able to confidently approve a proposal. In addition, a good level of detail will ease the design team's task of incorporating any changes into the project design. This alone will reduce resistance to implementation of the ideas.

Finally, proposals need to be comprehensive, as they are often reviewed by different types of audience. Representatives of the client may not be technically based in construction and, thus, proposals will need to be structured to provide lay persons with understanding, as well as providing the designers with sufficient technical information to make their evaluation.

Dilution of the development process can thus severely impair a VM study. When short cuts are made the potential results from the study are likely to be significantly reduced and the process is likely to leave a 'bad impression' with both the client and the design team. Bad impressions such as these are very difficult to overcome once formulated, and may cause the significant potential of VM to be unrealised by segments of the construction industry.

7.2   Typical Contents of a Proposal

Generally, a proposal will contain the following elements:

- Description of the original design
- Description of the proposed alternative design
- Advantages of the proposal
- Disadvantages of the proposal
- Discussion
- Life cycle cost implications
- Supporting technical backup.

A description of the original design is necessary as not all reviewers of the proposals will have full original design information readily accessible. Providing details of the original design will thus ease the review of the proposal, and therefore increase the potential for its acceptance.

A description of the proposed alternative design is necessary for obvious reasons. The description should be unambiguously stated to correctly convey the proposed change to the original design.

Advantages of the proposed change over the original design should be identified to highlight why the proposal should be accepted. These advantages should describe non-economic as well as economic aspects.

Disadvantages of the proposed change should be listed to ensure an appreciation of the downsides by decision makers. Writing up the disadvantages of a proposal also forces the VM team members to make an objective appraisal of their ideas, so that impracticable ideas can be weeded out.

A *discussion* of the proposal will include a number of elements. It can be used to provide a non-technical narrative of the reasoning behind the proposal which can be understood by non-technical decision makers. The implications of the proposed change with regard to other elements of the project or aspects such as the design and construction programme should be discussed. In addition, it is useful to discuss the procedure for implementing the proposal. This will assist decision makers as well as force the VM team members to consider whether implementation difficulties may negate the benefits of the proposal.

Life cycle cost implications of the proposals should be described. It is best to indicate initial costs and costs in use separately, as they will often be of differing importance to clients. While the main thrust of VM proposals is likely to be towards savings there are often occasions when additional costs result. These should be described in the same manner as cost savings.

When there is insufficient information available to reasonably cost proposals or the design is not sufficiently developed to know for sure that a proposal would be enacted anyway the change may be put forward as a design suggestion. Wherever possible proposals should be costed so that decision making information is maximised. The number of design suggestions should therefore be kept to a minimum and used judiciously: the term should not be used to disguise a proposal that results in additional cost.

Supporting technical backup must be prepared to ensure that the proposal is valid. This backup should be supplied as part of the proposal to ease the technical review by the original design team and to assure their full understanding of what is being proposed. The backup should consist of applicable sketches and design calculations such as structural or mechanical load calculations, and the like. References for relevant specification sections, catalogue information, design standards and building regulations, etc. should be provided. When information is sourced externally from suppliers or consultants, the *source* and *contact* details should be provided to enable verification. Finally, all *cost calculations* should be clearly stated.

As clarity and comprehensiveness are essential, the VMTC should review all proposals as they are developed and direct any amendments or amplifications needed before the team members who wrote them leave the workshop.

7.3   Estimating Costs

In VM the *total life cycle costs* of proposals are considered. These comprise the initial capital costs of design and construction, as well as the present value of costs in use such as operations and maintenance costs, as well as the present value of costs for the occasional replacement of elements such as mechanical equipment. The procedure for calculating cost in use is discussed later in this chapter. This section will thus concentrate on initial costs.

Whenever possible, the initial cost of proposals should be calculated using cost data such as unit rates and the like, from the existing or reconciled cost estimate. Full details regarding quantities and sources of cost data, etc. should be included with the cost calculations that are provided as backup to the proposal. When there is insufficient cost data available from the existing estimate, data may be obtained from the VM team estimator's own database, published sources of pricing data or from suppliers.

It is best to err on the conservative side and report marginally *lower* savings than to report inflated savings: where proposed savings are considered inflated by design team members it will cast doubt on the validity of the proposals. Due to the time constraints of the study the pricing may need to be approximate in nature. When there is a need for a high degree of estimating accuracy, it may be worthwhile to supplement the VM team estimator with additional estimators during the Development phase. If the VM team estimator is the sole team member costing the proposals, he or she may soon become swamped in proposals that are being prepared by the various disciplines. It is best if all the proposals can be costed during the study phase, as all the relevant technical expertise will be immediately available to provide answers to any questions the estimator may have. In addition, disruptions to the programme will be minimised.

If proposals are merely handed over to a cost consultant for pricing after the study there will be a considerable probability that misunderstandings will invalidate some of the estimated costs. Such a situation should therefore be avoided.

The close interactive nature of the study conditions will ensure that realistic estimating can be achieved and it is, thus, preferable for all the costing to be completed by the end of the study phase.

7.4   Life Cycle Costing

Introduction

As stated in Chapter 2, Life cycle costing (LCC) is a key component of authentic VM. LCC can be considered to be a methodology in its own right and is, indeed, the subject of a number of books which give it detailed attention. In view of the comprehensive nature of coverage in other books, this section is intended to provide only a broad overview of LCC techniques, and how they are applied in VM. For readers requiring a more in depth understanding of the subject, we would encourage them to refer to some of the books dedicated to LCC, some of which, such as Ferry and Flanagan (1991) and Seeley (1983), are listed in the References (p. 221).

What is LCC?

LCC entails the calculation of costs applying to the *total life cycle* of the facility. In addition to the initial costs of a project such as the design and construction costs, ongoing costs such as operations and maintenance of the completed facility are considered. As the various costs are incurred over a long time horizon, a method known as *discounting* is used to bring all costs to a comparable level. Discounting resolves the complication that an amount spent today is not necessarily comparable to an equivalent amount spent at a future date due to the fact that interest may have been earned on the earlier expenditure. Thus £100 today will be worth more than £100 in a year from now as interest could have accrued on it for a period of a year.

Why is LCC Important?

It is important to apply LCC techniques during design as the design solutions selected may have major implications for the operational and maintenance costs of the completed facility. These operational and maintenance costs are usually incurred for a long period, and often collectively far outweigh the initial capital costs of the facility. There are often occasions when a modification in design can cause a minor increase in initial construction costs, but also give rise to savings in operations and maintenance costs which dwarf that additional cost.

It is often argued that the importance of LCC on a particular project will depend on the nature of the client for that project. For example, a developer who constructs a facility for immediate sale is less likely to be concerned with ongoing operations and maintenance costs than a client who intends to occupy or utilise the facility upon its completion. While there is undoubtedly a good basis for such an argument, it is likely that LCC will continue to grow in importance even for purely speculative developers as occupiers' awareness of the implications of design on operations and maintenance grows. Indeed, the astute developer may use low LCC as a selling point whether selling, leasing or renting out the facility.

What Costs are Involved in LCC?

As described, the total costs from the inception of a project to the final disposal of the facility are considered in LCC. The main elements of cost are indicated in Working Document 7.1 and are described below.

Initial costs involve:

- The cost of feasibility studies
- Land acquisition
- Professional fees for design, project management, legal advice, etc.
- Construction and furnishings and fittings.

These costs are normally well established and are often focused upon when making decisions about the project.

Operations costs may be divided into two broad levels: *general* and *functional*. General costs are those related to aspects such as cleaning, fuel/electricity, insurance and security and the like. Each of these costs may be significantly affected by design decisions.

- *Cleaning costs* will be impacted on by the materials chosen. For example, if fixed windows are selected, external window cleaning via ladders or a window washing rig will be required. This is likely to cost more than if openable tilt/turn windows enabled cleaning from inside.

Working Document 7:1   Typical costs involved in LCC

COST TYPE	PROJECT STAGE	COST CATEGORIES			

INITIAL

Inception	Feasibility studies
Design	Land purchase
Construction	Professional fees
	Construction costs

OCCUPANCY/UTILISATION

Occupancy/utilisation	Operations	General	Cleaning
			Fuel/electricity
			Insurance
			Security
		Functional	Staffing
			Commercial rates
			Others
	Maintenance	Planned	Preventative
		Unplanned	Corrective
	Replacement/alterations		
	Taxation	Corporate	
		Allowances	
		VAT	

SALVAGE

| Disposal | Salvage, revenue & disposal costs |

- The *fuel and electricity costs* will differ according to broad design issues such as building volume or shape, operational parameters such as lighting levels, and temperature ranges, or, according to more detailed issues regarding the insulation efficiency of the external envelope or the efficiency of particular mechanical and electrical equipment specified.
- *Insurance costs* may be impacted by issues such as whether or not areas of the facility are sprinklered whilst
- *Security costs* are often impacted by facility configuration and by the number of access/egress points.

The second level of operational costs are related to the functional aspects of the facility. These costs include the *staffing* required to carry out the intended function of the facility: the design may significantly impact on the staffing requirements in certain facility types. A good indication of the extent of this impact comes from a value planning study conducted on a 500 cell prison project.

Case Example

During this study the VM team first proposed that the number of prisoners per housing unit could be increased, which dramatically reduced the number of guards due to the reduction in housing control rooms. Secondly, the number of guards required per prisoner was reduced further by strategically relocating the guard control booths.

Thirdly, the original design did not make provision for toilets in the cells, consequently guards would have to accompany prisoners to communal toilets during the night. The study proposed incorporating toilets into the cells, thus alleviating this requirement and again subsequently reducing guard staffing requirements. As the operation of a correctional facility required three staff shifts a day, 365 days a year, the annual savings in terms of staffing costs equated to millions of pounds, and when considered over the proposed life of the building, totally dwarfed any additional initial costs.

Staffing implications such as those described above are often paid minimal attention, but may have a critical impact on operations costs, particularly for heavily staffed institutional buildings such as prisons and hospitals.

Another operational cost which is often determined by the functional use of a facility is the cost of *commercial rates*. Rates can comprise a large percentage of overall operational costs. The level of rates expense will be determined largely by location of the facility, but also by classification of use. Thus, offices will incur different rates to manufacturing or warehouse facilities, and so on.

There are also a number of other costs associated with the functional use of a facility which must be determined on a project by project basis. For example, on a value planning study of a bus maintenance and storage facility, it was concluded that significant fuel costs could be saved by relocating the maintenance building within the site.

Case Example

The building served as a facility in which repairs and maintenance could be conducted, as well as providing refuelling and cleaning facilities. It was these latter functions, which occurred on a routine basis, that spurred the change in location. The original design required buses to go through a refuelling circuit from their storage location of several hundred metres. The revised location significantly reduced the average circuit length. When considering the number of buses affected together with the number of years that the buses would be using the facility, the fuel savings represented by the reductions in refuelling circuit lengths were significant enough to warrant relocation of the building.

It is in the area of functional operational costs that VM goes beyond other LCC exercises. More traditional LCC often purely focuses on the costs listed under the general level of operations, and ignores the huge potential costs associated with layout efficiency and similar factors. The potential in these areas lends further support to the inclusion of an operations expert on the VM team, as suggested earlier in this book.

Maintenance costs may also be divided into two broad levels – those deriving from planned or unplanned maintenance. *Planned* maintenance encompasses preventive maintenance activities such as lubricating equipment, as well as planned correctional activities which may be conducted during a shutdown of a process-type facility. *Unplanned* maintenance encompasses corrective action which may have to be undertaken on an emergency basis, such as repairing a breakdown of refrigeration equipment in a supermarket. While planned maintenance costs may be satisfactorily estimated, the costs for unplanned maintenance will be difficult to forecast. In general, it is likely the maintenance costs will increase with the age of the facility or its constituent elements and equipment.

Replacement and alteration costs are periodic costs that occur once every so often. Replacement costs include the costs of replacing elements of the facility or items of equipment that reach the end of their useful life before the end of the facility's life. For example, a typical flat roof membrane may require replacement after 15 years or the cooling tower associated with an air conditioning system may have deteriorated to such an extent that it requires replacement after 20 years.

Alterations costs have more to do with the *functional use* of a facility, and may be more difficult to forecast than replacement costs. Alterations comprise changes to the facility that are desired for functional purposes, such as the reconfiguration of departments in an office. Where it is envisaged that the functional use of a facility is likely to change relatively frequently during its life, then consideration should be given to incorporating flexibility in the design. Typical examples of such flexibility might include designing a modular lighting layout, using demountable partitions, and so on.

Taxation costs must be considered in LCC to the extent that they may be recoverable from tax allowances against certain items of expenditure. Expenditures on maintenance and operations may be deducted from the amount upon which a company is taxed and consequently reduce taxation levels. The relative advantages of increased expenditure of capital, i.e. initial costs against reduced occupational or utilisation costs and vice versa, is complex. The inclusion of taxation expertise on a VM team may thus make sense, particularly for large projects.

Salvage revenue and disposal costs refer respectively to any revenue that may be obtained from the sale of a facility or item of equipment at the end of the facility's life, and to the costs of disposal of a facility or item of equipment arising from demolition or removal.

Information Needs and Sources

The information needed for LCC varies from project to project, and according to the element or component being studied. The main items of data that are generally required are described below together with their respective potential sources.

Discount rates are the rates to be applied during discounting exercises to bring future costs to a comparable basis. In essence, the discount rate will be the client's cost of money. While VM studies often use the current interest rate for borrowing, this does not necessarily equate to the client's cost of money. The calculation of this rate will be complex, requiring the consideration of differing proportions of costs related to debt, i.e. loans, and equity, i.e. investment, together with issues such as risk, taxation rates and predicted interest and inflation rates.

The discount rate will have a profound affect on the LCC calculations and thus must be carefully selected. A high discount rate produces results that favour alternatives which have high initial costs and low annual occupancy/ utilisation costs and a short life. Low discount rates will produce results which favour the opposite alternatives.

Bearing in mind the complexity involved in establishing discount rates, together with the importance of getting it right, this information is best obtained from the client organisation.

Life predictions are also necessary for LCC exercises, for two reasons. First, the expected life of the facility is needed so that a boundary may be put on the timescale up to which future costs are considered. This information should obviously come from the client.

Secondly, the expected life of individual elements or components of a facility is needed to establish when in the future those elements and components will need to be replaced. Thus, the life of a roof membrane may be established at 20 years, after which it will be replaced. This information may be obtained from manufacturers, from the client's maintenance personnel or from VM or design team members. Careful judgement should be applied to these life predictions, as manufacturers may be inclined to exaggerate whilst predictions from maintenance personnel and design team members will only be as good as the experience upon which they have based their forecasts.

Cost data is required for both capital one-off expenditures as well as ongoing annual expenditures. Cost data for capital expenditure involved with initial costs for construction, etc. or for replacement of elements or components during the facility's life may be obtained from well established databases compiled by quantity surveying or cost engineering firms or from published cost data sources.

Data for ongoing annual costs may be more difficult to obtain, and require the pursuit of a number of sources. One of the most important annual costs is for *fuel* and *energy*. As rates may fluctuate among different organisations, depending on their use levels, the best source of this information is probably the client. Where the client does not have this information the various costs for electricity, gas, oil, and so on may be obtained directly from the suppliers of those utilities. Other ongoing costs associated with operational aspects such as staffing, insurance, commercial rates, and so on should be obtained from the client.

Data for *maintenance costs* is probably the most difficult to obtain, as it is not easy to predict the level of maintenance effort required for different elements or components. Increasingly, owners of numerous facilities are incorporating building management systems in their new projects which have connections to recording devices on major items of equipment. Where these recording devices are available the client may have established some maintenance cost databases. It is, however, rare that a client will have such a database and thus other sources are usually relied upon. Typical sources are manufacturers, maintenance personnel and the VM or design team. Again, the reliability of information from the maintenance personnel and the VM or design team is directly related to their level of experience, and information from manufacturers may be optimistic, so it should be used cautiously. Published historical data from Building Maintenance Ltd (formerly Building Maintenance Cost Information Service, BMCIS) may be used in place of, or as verification of, data obtained from the above sources. Another possible source of information is from any *maintenance agreements* the client may have with contractors.

Discounting Techniques

There are two discounting techniques commonly applied during LCC exercises in connection with VM studies. The most common is the Net Present Value (NPV) method whereby all costs and revenues are calculated to present day values and totalled into a single sum. The other common method is the Annualised Equivalent Value (AEV) method whereby instead of calculating a single sum representing the NPV, all costs and revenues are presented as an annual equivalent value which would occur uniformly through the life of the facility. Either technique will arrive at the same ranking of alternatives, but the NPV method permits easier consideration of inflation, and is therefore preferred.

While formulae are available for the calculation of discount factors to be applied to future costs in order to bring them to present values, it is far easier, and thus more usual, to use *standard interest rate tables* to establish these factors. For convenience some of these standard tables are included in this book in Appendix 1, together with the formulae used to formulate them.

Brief, simplified examples below show how each technique may be applied.

Net Present Value (NPV)

For the sake of this example suppose two items of equipment, Contraption *A* and Contraption *B*, which both perform the same function, are being compared in terms of life cycle costs.

The methodology to be applied to calculate the NPV will be as follows:

Step 1:   Establish study parameters such as discount rate and facility life, etc.

Step 2:   Determine initial cost

Step 3:   Determine periodic costs such as replacement of worn out components every so many years

Apply the appropriate factor from the Present Value of £1 Table to discount these future costs to present value (see Appendix 1).

Step 4:   Determine annual costs such as the cost of fuel or energy to run the items of equipment

Apply the appropriate factor from the Present Value of £1 per Annum Table to discount these future costs to a single present value (see Appendix 1)

Step 5:   Establish salvage revenue or disposal costs such as revenue from the sale of equipment to other prospective users at the end of the facility life or the cost to demolish the items of equipment

Apply the appropriate factor from the Present Value of £1 Table to discount the future revenue to the present value

Step 6:   Total the present values of the initial costs, periodic costs, annual costs and salvage revenues or disposal costs to obtain the *NPV for each item of equipment.*

Thus, assuming the discount rate to be used is 10%, the facility life is determined as 10 years and that the various costs are as shown in Working Document 7.2, then the NPVs for each Contraption would be calculated as shown in Working Document 7.3.

Annual Equivalent Value (AEV)

The methodology to be applied to calculate the AEV will be as follows:

Step 1:   Establish study parameters such as discount rate and facility life, etc.
Step 2:   Determine initial costs
Step 3:   Determine periodic costs and salvage revenue/disposal costs and apply appropriate factor from the Present Value of £1 Table to discount these future costs to the present value
Step 4:   Determine annual costs
Step 5:   Convert present values for initial costs periodic costs and salvage revenues/disposal costs to annualised equivalent costs
Apply the appropriate factor from the annuities table (see Appendix 1)
Step 6:   Total the annualised initial and periodic costs to the annual costs to obtain the *total annual equivalent costs.*

Working Document 7.2   Costs used in NPV and AEV examples

	Contraption *A*	Contraption *B*
Initial cost	20 000	17 000
Periodic costs		
Replace component *x* in year 6		3000
Replace component *y* in year 7	2000	
Replace component *z* in year 8	1500	
Annual costs		
Energy (electrical) costs	1500	2000
Maintenance costs	500	750
Salvage revenue/disposal costs Assuming revenue will be realised from sale of the secondhand contraptions	2000	1700

Working Document 7.3   Example of a NPV calculation

			Contraption A	Contraption B
STEP 1 Discount rate: 10% Facility life: 10 years				
STEP 2 Initial costs			20 000.00	17 000.00
STEP 3 Periodic costs		PV factor from PV of £1 table		
Replace component x in year 6	3000	0.5645		1693.50
Replace component y in year 7	2000	0.5132	1026.40	
Replace component z in year 8	1500	0.4665	699.75	
STEP 4 Annual costs		PV factor from PV of £1 per annum table (for 10 years)		
Contraption A: Energy	1500	6.145	9217.50	
Maintenance	500	6.145	3072.50	
Contraption B: Energy	2000	6.145		12 290.00
Maintenance	750	6.145		4608.75
STEP 5 Salvage revenue		PV factor from PV of £1 table		
Contraption A:	2000	0.3855	(771.00)	
Contraption B:	1700	0.3855		(655.35)
STEP 6 Total Net Present Value			33 245.15	34 936.90

Note: For calculations, see Standard Interest Rate Tables in Appendix 1.

Thus, assuming the same data as used for the previous NPV example, the AEV of each alternative would be determined as shown in Working Document 7.4.

Usual Methods Used to Compare Alternatives in VM

The easiest and most common method of comparison is to compare the NPV or AEV of proposed alternatives and select the alternative with the lowest LCC. Thus, in the previous examples, Contraption A would be the selected

Working Document 7.4   Example of a AEV calculation

			Contraption A	Contraption B
STEP 1				
Discount rate: 10%				
Facility life: 10 years				
STEP 2				
Initial costs			20 000.00	17 000.00
STEP 3				
Periodic costs		PV factor from PV of £1 table		
Replace component x in year 6	3000.00	0.5645		1693.50
Replace component y in year 7	2000.00	0.5132	1026.40	
Replace component z in year 8	1500.00	0.4665	699.75	
STEP 4				
Annual costs				
Energy			1500.00	2000.00
Maintenance			500.00	750.00
STEP 5		Factor from compound interest for annuities table		
Initial costs				
Contraption A	20 000.00	0.163	3260.00	
Contraption B	17 000.00	0.163		2771.00
Periodic costs				
Replace component x in year 6	1693.50	0.163	276.04	
Replace component y in year 7	1026.40	0.163		167.30
Replace component z in year 8	699.75	0.163		114.06
Salvage revenue				
Contraption A	(771.00)	0.163	(125.67)	
Contraption B	(655.35)	0.163		(106.82)
STEP 6				
Total Annual Equivalent Value			5410.37	5695.54

Note: For calculations, see Standard Interest Rate Tables in Appendix 1.

item of equipment despite having the highest initial cost because when the LCCs are compared it is the favourable option.

Other Comparative Methods

While not generally applicable to VM exercises, there are other comparative methods which may be encountered. These are included here to provide a minimal level of familiarisation.

One such method used when the LCC is a combination of costs and revenues is the discounted *Internal Rate of Return* (IRR). The IRR is the discount rate that must be applied to achieve an NPV of zero. This discount rate is found by trial and error. Thus, when comparing alternatives the one with the higher IRR would be preferred. One major flaw of IRR for comparison is that the two alternatives may be of very different amounts. Thus, an IRR of 10% earned on £100 is not worth as much as an IRR of 5% on £1000. The lower worth option would, however, be selected on the basis of IRR comparison alone. For this and other reasons the IRR is not recommended as a method for comparison of alternatives during LCC exercises.

Other comparison methods such as the *discounted payback method* and the *discounted savings to investment ratio* may be useful from time to time. Both methods are most suitable when an initial expenditure will derive savings in the future: for example, insulating an external wall may reduce future energy costs.

The payback method calculates the time taken for an expenditure to be covered by savings, i.e. the period of time up to an NPV of zero. Here the deciding factor between alternatives may be the selection of the one that achieves an NPV quickest. It should be noted, however, that in the long run, that alternative would not necessarily have the lowest LCC.

The savings to investment ratio is merely calculated by dividing the forecast savings by the amount of investment required to achieve those savings. Thus, if it costs £500 to insulate external walls, but the present value of savings over a defined period is £1000, then the savings to investment ratio would be £1000 ÷ £500 = 2. Obviously, the higher the ratio the more attractive the solution. The problem with this method is similar to that with the IRR, in that the comparison of various alternatives' ratios will not indicate the total amount of savings derived from each alternative.

Problems with LCC and Mitigating Measures

A number of problems have been cited by various authors regarding the realistic application of LCC. While these problems are indeed valid, there are ways to mitigate their impact so that LCC remains a highly worthwhile effort. The main problems and measures to overcome or mitigate those problems are now described.

Unrealistic discount rates

Bearing in mind the complexity of establishing discount rates, there is scepticism about whether a realistic discount rate can be established. The discount rate has a profound impact on the LCC calculations, and the application of different discount rates may cause different rankings of alternatives. A way to mitigate this problem is to use *sensitivity tests* having undertaken the LCC exercise based on the proposed discount rate. This sensitivity test will involve checking how sensitive the rankings of alternatives are to the discount rate by calculating the LCC at rates above and below that originally proposed. The rankings would be considered to be highly sensitive if they were altered by a 1% change in discount rates or insensitive if a change of several per cent or more did not alter the rankings of alternatives. By gauging the level of sensitivity of rankings one can objectively assess the validity of the selection of a particular alternative.

Differential inflation rates

While the consideration of inflation rates is not necessary when it is at a common level for all items of expenditure, it is unlikely that such as situation would ever exist in reality. A more realistic situation is one whereby certain items, say fuel costs, will be escalating more quickly than other items such as bricks and mortar. If these differences are not accounted for, then the results of the LCC exercise may be unrealistic. This problem may be overcome by allowing for inflation rate differentials for only those items of cost that are escalating at a different rate to that of general inflation.

Lifespan uncertainty

The lifespan for both the facility and various components of the facility need to be forecasted for LCC. Each forecast will involve different uncertainties which may invalidate them.

First, the estimate of facility life, which is usually provided by the client organisation based on its expected period of use of the facility, does not take account of the possibility of *early obsolescence* due to physical, socio–economic, or technological reasons. Premature obsolescence may occur due to reasons such as physical deterioration, changing socio–economic environments (e.g., the relative obsolescence of high rise residential accommodation built in the 1960s due to social aversion), or a change in technologies that may mean that a different facility configuration may achieve a function more economically. A way to mitigate such problems is to reduce the period over which the LCC is considered. Thus, when considering a facility which is expected to serve a functional purpose for 60 years, the LCC may be considered only over a 20 year period. Indeed, it has been proposed that a 25 year period may be a reasonable maximum facility life for all LCC purposes.

Secondly, the estimates of life for various components of the facility are subject to a fairly high degree of uncertainty. For example, predictions regarding when an item of equipment may be so physically deteriorated that it requires replacement may be difficult to make accurately. Furthermore, a more technologically advanced item of equipment may be developed which, for reasons of improved efficiency, may replace the original item of equipment even though it is not at the end of its physical life. Again, the way to mitigate such problems may be to shorten the timespan over which the LCC for alternative equipment items are considered. Thus, rather than considering the equipment over the total lifespan of the facility of say 25 years, one might only use a period of five years as the basis for LCC.

Estimating uncertainties

Any estimate of future cost is, by its very nature, uncertain. While this uncertainty can be reduced for some areas of costs by basing forecasts on historical data, other areas of cost, such as maintenance, have little historical data to assist estimation. The mitigation for this problem is that LCC should be considered as an order of magnitude exercise, rather than a precise one. Thus, while LCC may not give the exact cost of future expenditures, it should be able to provide at a broad level a relative ranking between alternatives. Such a ranking must be viewed judiciously. The Federal government in the USA, for example, considers economic analyses indeterminate if they indicate a difference of less than 10% between alternatives.

Capital versus revenue responsibilities

In many organisations the responsibilities for capital and revenue budgets are divided between different parties. For construction projects, which typically represent large capital expenditures, organisations will frequently assign in-house 'project managers' who will be responsible for the particular projects. This responsibility extends to managing the capital cost of the project, but rarely involves any accountability for the long-term occupancy/utilisation costs. This situation tends to orient those project managers to favour design solutions that may minimise initial capital costs at the expense of escalating future occupancy/utilisation costs. Obviously in the long run this state of affairs does not benefit the organisation, as alternatives with higher life cycle costs than necessary will be selected.

This lack of combined responsibility for capital and revenue costs is perhaps the primary reason that LCC is not applied on more projects. A VM study, however, may solve this potential problem if attention is paid to the study by senior management. When senior management becomes involved in the review of VM proposals, as is recommended elsewhere in this book, then they are more likely to take a long-term view and be swayed toward lower life cycle cost options.

The examples of NPV and AEV calculations included earlier in the chapter were simplistic for explanatory purposes. The two Case Examples which follow are more indicative of the types of LCC exercise that may be undertaken in real life.

Case Example 1: Comparison of Lifts

This first example applies to a LCC comparison between a hydraulic versus traction lift required for a local authority facility. The specification required a lift which served three floors with a velocity of 0.63 m/second and a capacity for eight people and 600–650 kg in weight. The interior finish requirements were basic.

The selection of which lift to use was to be based on the NPV which represented the lowest LCC option. A discount rate of 6% was used and the analysis was based on a 25 year duration.

The initial costs for each option were calculated as described in Working Document 7.5.

The periodic costs involved were for intermittent maintenance costs which were calculated as shown on Working Document 7.6.

The annual costs included both operational energy costs and routine maintenance contract costs. The energy costs were calculated on the basis of the equation:

Annual energy cost =
Connected load (kw) × Diversity factor × Hours available for use per year × Tariff
(£/p)

It was assumed for the purposes of calculating the operational time per year that the lift motors would be running constantly during the periods the lifts were available for use, i.e. 14 hours per day in this example.

The routine maintenance costs were calculated as follows:

Option A Quarterly Inspection by Lift Engineers:
2 men x 4 hours x £15/hour x 4 visits = *£480.*
Option B Quarterly Inspection by Lift Engineers:
2 men x 7 hours x £15/hour x 4 visits = *£840.*

Working Document 7.5 Calculation of initial costs for lift options

	OPTION *A* HYDRAULIC PASSENGER LIFT		OPTION *B* TWO SPEED AC PASSENGER LIFT	
	Dimensions (m)	Cost £	Dimensions (m)	Cost £
Supply and installation		22 750		27 500
Lift pit	2.2x1.7x1.4	2750	2.2x1.7x1.7	3 500
Machine room	2x3x2.6 (ground floor)	1500	2.5x3.7x2.6 (upper floor)	6 000
Lift shaft	75m^2	4000	95m^2	6 650
Preliminaries		3500		5 000
Total initial cost		**34 500**		**48 650**

Working Document 7.6   Calculation of intermittent maintenance costs

OPTION A: HYDRAULIC LIFT

Year	1	2	3	4	5	6	7	8	9	10
Component										
Governors					1000					3000
Guide shoes						1500				
Electric relays/Contacts		200			200			200		
Car refurbishment					3000					5000
Landing doors and car door components							750			
Ram seals						2000				
Hydraulic fluid					1000					1000
Signals and controller				500				500		
Pit equipment					200					1000
Strip out										
Totals £	**0**	**0**	**200**	**500**	**5200**	**2200**	**2250**	**500**	**200**	**10 000**

OPTION B: TWO SPEED AC LIFT

Year	1	2	3	4	5	6	7	8	9	10
Component										
Governors					1000					3000
Supervision ropes							4000			
Guide shoes							1500			
Electric relays/Contacts		200			200			200		
Car refurbishment					3000					5000
Landing doors and car door components							700			
Signals and controller				500				500		
Pit equipment					200					1000
Strip out										
Totals £	**0**	**0**	**200**	**500**	**4200**	**200**	**6200**	**500**	**200**	**6200**

11	12	13	14	15	16	17	18	19	20	21	22	23	24	25
				1000					3000					
			1500							1500				
	200			200			200			200			200	
				3000					5000					
										750				
			4000											
	2000						2000						2000	
				1000					1000					
	500				500				500				500	
				200					1000					
														8000
0	2700	0	5500	5400	500	0	2200	0	10 500	2450	0	0	2700	8000

11	12	13	14	15	16	17	18	19	20	21	22	23	24	25
				1000					3000					
			4000							4000				
			1500							1500				
	200			200			200			200			200	
				3000					5000					
			4000							750				
	500				500				500				500	
				200					1000					
														10 000
0	700	0	9500	4400	500	0	200	0	9500	6450	0	0	700	10 000

It was considered that the lifts would have no salvage value at the end of 25 years and cost for demolition (or stripping out) were included in the calculation of intermittent maintenance costs. As the client was a local authority, no adjustments were necessary for taxation allowances.

Having determined all the amounts for the various types of cost these were entered onto a spreadsheet using a computer in order to calculate present values. This spreadsheet is shown in Working Document 7.7. With the common usage of computer spreadsheet packages today, it is usually easier to calculate present values in this manner rather than manually. It is desirable therefore to have access to a computer during a VM study.

Case Example 2:   Comparison of Air Conditioning Equipment

A client had taken over an existing office complex and was undertaking a series of projects to refurbish existing buildings as well as to build additional facilities.

The existing air conditioning system was based on 4 x 750 kw water-cooled chillers, located in a central energy centre outside the complex. Two of the chillers use R11 refrigerant and two use R22 refrigerant. R11 refrigerant is a CFC which, under the Montreal Protocol, is currently being phased out. As other projects were ongoing and the existing equipment needed refurbishment anyway, it was decided that the chillers using R11 should be replaced.

Two options were put forward for comparison:

- Refurbish the two R22 machines and replace the two R11 machines with new ones using refrigerant R134A, a more environmentally acceptable refrigerant.
- Refurbish the two R22 machines, replace the two R11 machines with one R134A machine and use the chillers in conjunction with an ice storage system to generate ice at night using off peak electricity. The stored ice will then be used during the day to provide a considerable portion of the cooling load in summer and most of the cooling load in spring and autumn.

For the purposes of calculating the LCCs for each option a discount rate of 6% was used. As only a comparison of LCCs for each option was required costs which were considered to be the same for both options (e.g., cleaning and cooling tower maintenance) were ignored. As the client's usual investment criteria involved a requirement for payback within five years, the period for analysis was set at five years.

The initial costs for each option were calculated as described in Working Document 7.8.

Working Document 7.8   Calculation of initial costs for AC equipment options

	OPTION *A* Conventional chilled water £	OPTION *B* Ice storage £
Remove and dispose of R11 chillers	10 000	10 000
Overhaul existing R22 chillers	45 000	45 000
Supply and install new chiller(s)	155 000	80 000
Ice storage tanks, pipework, valves and pumps	0	128 000
Pumps – primary/secondary	12 000	12 000
Pipework, valves and insulation	48 000	58 000
Electrical services and controls	40 000	55 000
Sundries	3000	5000
Testing and commissioning	5000	6000
Builders' work in connection	3000	14 000
Installation total	**321 000**	**413 000**
Preliminaries	9000	12 000
Professional fees	20 000	25 000
Total cost	**350 000**	**450 000**

Due to the short time period for the analysis, periodic costs for replacement of components, etc. were not considered relevant. In addition, residual values were not considered pertinent to the final decision between the systems, and were thus not included in the calculations.

The annual costs included both energy costs and routine maintenance costs which were calculated as shown in Working Documents 7.9, 7.10 and 7.11.

As the client was a private corporation, tax allowances were relevant and were calculated as shown in Working Document 7.12 and VAT was ignored as it was assumed that incoming and outgoing VAT would cancel each other out.

Having determined all the amounts for the various types of cost, they were entered onto a spreadsheet to calculate the net present costs for each option as shown in Working Document 7.13.

Conclusions

An orientation towards the consideration of total life cycle costs is a key component of VM which should be adhered to wherever possible.

While it is unlikely that all VM proposals will require the calculation of LCCs, they should always be considered. For some proposals the cost savings in terms of occupation/utilisation costs of a facility or element may far exceed any additional initial costs. By identifying both initial costs and costs in use for

Working Document 7.7   *Calculation of present values for lift options using a spreadsheet*

OPTION A: HYDRAULIC LIFT

Year	0	1	2	3	4	5	6	7	8	9	10
Costs (£000)											
Capital	38 000										
Operational		764	764	764	764	764	764	764	764	764	764
Intermittent maintenance		0	0	200	500	5200	2200	2250	500	200	10 000
Annual maintenance		480	480	480	480	480	480	480	480	480	480
Total	38 000	1244	1244	1444	1744	6444	3444	3494	1744	1444	11 244
Discount factor @ 6%		0.94	0.89	0.84	0.79	0.75	0.71	0.67	0.63	0.59	0.56
Present Value £	38 000	1169	1107	1213	1378	4833	2445	2341	1099	852	6297
TOTAL PRESENT VALUE £80 960											

OPTION B: TWO SPEED AC LIFT

Year	0	1	2	3	4	5	6	7	8	9	10
Costs (£000)											
Capital	53 150										
Operational		437	437	437	437	437	437	437	437	437	437
Intermittent maintenance		0	0	200	500	4200	200	6200	500	200	9000
Annual maintenance		840	840	840	840	840	840	840	840	840	840
Total	53 150	1277	1277	1477	1777	5477	1477	7477	1777	1477	10 277
Discount factor @ 6%		0.94	0.89	0.84	0.79	0.75	0.71	0.67	0.63	0.59	0.56
Present Value £	53 150	1200	1137	1241	1404	4108	1049	5010	1120	871.4	5755
TOTAL PRESENT VALUE £96 898											

11	12	13	14	15	16	17	18	19	20	21	22	23	24	25
764	764	764	764	764	764	764	764	764	764	764	764	764	764	764
0	2700	0	5500	5400	500	0	2200	0	10 500	2450	0	0	2700	8000
480	480	480	480	480	480	480	480	480	480	480	480	480	480	480
1244	3944	1244	6744	6644	1744	1244	3444	1244	11 744	3694	1244	1244	3944	9244
0.53	0.5	0.47	0.44	0.42	0.39	0.37	0.35	0.33	0.31	0.29	0.28	0.26	0.25	0.23
659	1972	585	2967	2790	680	460	1205	410.5	3641	1071	348	323	986	2126

11	12	13	14	15	16	17	18	19	20	21	22	23	24	25
437	437	437	437	437	437	437	437	437	437	437	437	437	437	437
0	700	0	9500	4400	500	0	200	0	9500	6450	0	0	700	10 000
840	840	840	840	840	840	840	840	840	840	840	840	840	840	840
1277	1977	1277	10 777	5677	1777	1277	1477	1277	10 777	7727	1277	1277	1977	11 277
0.53	0.5	0.47	0.44	0.42	0.39	0.37	0.35	0.33	0.31	0.29	0.28	0.26	0.25	0.23
677	989	600	4742	2384	693	472	517	421.4	3341	2241	358	332	494	2594

Working Document 7.9   Basis of assessment of energy costs for refrigeration plant

1. Occupied operating period – 0800 hrs to 1800 hrs, 5 days per week for 43 weeks per year
2. Building peak cooling load – 2670Kw
3. Power factor – 0.9
4. Based on EEB MD6 HV maximum demand tariffs

ESTIMATION OF REFRIGERATION PLANT CAPACITY
OPTION A

Equipment	No.	Power input each Kw	Total power input Kw	Summer load factor	Summer power input	Winter load factor	Winter power input
Existing water cooled chillers	2	162	324	0.6	195	0.3	97
New water cooled chillers	2	273	546	0.6	328	0.3	164
Existing chilled water distribution pumps	4	19	76	1	76	1	76
Existing condenser water distribution pumps	4	19	76	1	76	1	76
Cooling tower fans	2	45	90	0.7	63	0.3	27
Total			1112 Kw		738 Kw		440 Kw

OPTION B

Equipment	No.	Power input each Kw	Total power input Kw	Summer load factor		Summer power input		Winter load factor		Winter power input	
				Day	Night	Day	Night	Day	Night	Day	Night
Existing water cooled chillers	2	134	268	0.3	0.8	81	214	0	0.6	0	161
New water cooled chillers	1	328	328	0.3	0.8	99	262	0	0.6	0	197
Existing chilled water distribution pumps	4	19	76	1	0.8	76	61	1	0.6	76	46
New Ice Storage Distribution Pumps	1	15	15	1	0.8	15	12	1	0.6	15	9
Existing condenser water distribution pumps	3	19	57	1	0.8	57	46	1	0.6	57	34
Cooling tower fans	2	45	90	0.3	0.3	27	27	0	0.6	0	54
Total			834 Kw			355 Kw	622 Kw			148 Kw	501 Kw

Working Document 7.10   Calculation of annual energy costs for AC equipment

Operating period

Summer day	26 wks × 5 days × 10 hrs = 1300 hrs
Summer night	26 wks × 5 days × 7 hrs = 910 hrs
Winter day	17 wks × 5 days × 10 hrs = 850 hrs
Winter night	17 wks × 5 days × 7 hrs = 595 hrs

Item	OPTION A		OPTION B	
	Calculation	Total £	Calculation	Total £
Standing charge	10 months × 105.37	1054	10 months × 105.37	1054
Availability charge	6 months × 1.03 × 1112/0.9 4 months × 1.03 × 1112/0.9	7636 5090	6 months × 1.03 × 834/0.9 4 months × 1.03 × 834/0.9	5727 3818
Maximum demand charge	2 months × 2.17 × 1112/0.9	5363	2 months × 2.17 × 834/0.9	4022
Unit charges	1300 × 5.32p × 738/0.9 850 × 5.32p × 440/0.9	56 711 22 108	1300 × 5.32p × 355/0.9 910 × 2.45p × 622/0.9 850 × 5.32p × 148/0.9 595 × 2.45p × 501/0.9	27 280 15 408 7436 8115
Total Annual Energy Costs		**97 962**		**72 860**

Working Document 7.11 *Calculation of costs for annual maintenance of AC equipment*

	OPTION A £	OPTION B £
Maintenance requirements		
General maintenance	6000	4500
@ £1500/ chiller		
Pumps – monthly inspection	1440	1440
8 × 1 hr × 12 month × £15/hr		
Pumps – quarterly strip down	2880	2880
8 × 6 hrs ×4 × £15/hr		
Consumables allowance	500	500
Total Costs per Annum	**10 820**	**9320**
	say £11 000	**say £9500**

proposals, decision makers are given information which enables them to understand the *long-term*, and not just *immediate*, consequences of their decisions.

In VM it is important to consider costs associated with *functional* aspects of a facility such as staffing as well as the *operations* and *maintenance* costs traditionally considered in LCC exercises. Costs associated with functional aspects may be huge.

While there are problems associated with the applications of LCC techniques, they can be overcome with judicious use and should not, therefore, be used as an excuse for not considering an LCC exercise.

The consideration of LCC offers a broader scope for the improvement of value than would be the case if only initial costs were considered. A mere orientation towards LCC may sometimes cause a VM team to question fundamental issues relating to a project which would not otherwise have been challenged. A rather extreme Case Example of such an event is as follows.

Case Example

The subject of this example is a VP study that was conducted in connection with a large unloading facility for a rubbish disposal facility. It was a very large facility, with an estimated cost of approximately £60 million.

When the project had been originally conceived, the rubbish disposal facility had a substantial remaining life. However, for a variety of reasons, development of the project had been delayed so that by the time of the VP study there only remained a few years of useful life after the forecast completion

Working Document 7.12   Calculation of taxation allowances for AC equipment comparison

All taxation allowances were assumed to arise in the year following the expenditure to which they relate and a general price deflator of 5% was assumed to convert them from nominal to real terms

Corporation tax: 33%
Capital allowance: 25% reducing Balance (an alternative to straight line depreciation)
Annual price deflator: 5%

	OPTION A (Capital cost £350 000)	OPTION B (Capital cost £450 000)
Capital allowances		
Year 1 (Capital cost × 25% × 33%) / 1.05	27 500	35 357
Year 2 (Capital cost × 75% × 25% × 33%)/ 1.05	19 643	25 255
Year 3 (Capital cost × 75% × 25% × 33%)/ 1.05	14 031	18 039
Year 4 (Capital cost × 75% × 25% × 33%)/ 1.05	11 601	13 529
Year 5 (Capital cost × 75% × 25% × 33%)/ 1.05	8701	10 147
Revenue Allowances	(Annual Operating Costs) (£109 000)	(Annual Operating Costs) (£82 500)
(Annual Operating Costs x 33%)/ 1.05	34 257	25 929

Working Document 7.13   Calculation of present costs for AC equipment options using a spreadsheet

OPTION A – CONVENTIONAL CHILLED WATER SYSTEM

YEAR	0	1	2	3	4	5	6
COSTS (£)							
Capital	350 000						
Energy		98 000	98 000	98 000	98 000	98 000	
Maintenance		11 000	11 000	11 000	11 000	11 000	
Total	350 000	109 000	109 000	109 000	109 000	109 000	0
TAX ALLOWANCES (£)							
Capital	0	(27 500)	(20 000)	(14 000)	(10 000)	(7 000)	(5 000)
Revenue	0	0	(34 000)	(34 000)	(34 000)	(34 000)	(34 000)
Net total	350 000	81 500	55 000	61 000	65 000	68 000	(39 000)
Discount factor @ 6%	1	0.943	0.89	0.84	0.792	0.747	0.705
PRESENT COST (£)	350 000	77 000	49 000	51 000	51 000	51 000	(27 000)
TOTAL PRESENT COST	602 000						

OPTION B - ICE STORAGE SYSTEM

YEAR	0	1	2	3	4	5	6
COSTS (£)							
Capital	450 000						
Energy		73 000	73 000	73 000	73 000	73 000	
Maintenance		9 500	9 500	9 500	9 500	9 500	
Total	450 000	82 500	82 500	82 500	82 500	82 500	0
TAX ALLOWANCES (£)							
Capital	0	(35 000)	(25 000)	(18 000)	(13 000)	(9 000)	(7 000)
Revenue	0	0	(26 000)	(26 000)	(26 000)	(26 000)	(26 000)
Net Total	450 000	47 500	31 500	38 500	43 500	47 500	(33 000)
Discount factor @ 6%	1	0.943	0.89	0.84	0.792	0.747	0.705
PRESENT COST (£)	450 000	45 000	28 000	32 000	34 000	35 000	(23 000)
TOTAL PRESENT COST	601 000						

of the project. Obviously, the level of expenditure on the project was not justified by the shorter duration of the project's useful life.

After the VP team brought this problem to light the authority in charge of the project re-examined the whole concept. This re-examination subsequently resulted in a solution which extended the life of the disposal facility.

Thus, for VM purposes, possibly the greatest advantage of LCC is that it extends the scope of review to encompass broad issues beyond just the initial impact of the project. Merely being sensitised to future costs and consequences improves the likelihood of identifying *inherent issues and concerns* that might not otherwise be recognised.

8 Presentation Phase

8.1 Introduction

The objective of this final phase of the job plan is to assist in the communication of the results of the VM study to decision makers and the original design team. Since miscommunication of the proposals may result in their rejection, it is important that every effort is made to ensure full understanding of the VM team's recommendation by all interested parties. The Presentation phase enables the VM team to orally present their major recommendations so that the subsequent review of written proposals is not hindered by a lack of understanding.

It is good practice to give the oral presentation on the last day of the VM study before the VM team has been disbanded. This means that VM team members will be able to present or answer questions pertaining to their respective disciplines.

Generally, the audience will be divided into two distinct types. First, (where an external team has been used) there will be the original design team, who will be predominantly interested in the technical aspects of the various proposals. Secondly, there will be less technical attendees who may represent management decision makers, or other interested parties such as representatives of the operating staff of the final facility. It is very important that all decision makers are present, as it is critical that these people fully understand proposals so that they are able to make informed decisions.

As two types of audiences are involved the presentation should be prepared to cater to both of their needs. Presentations of proposals will require both technical as well as broad narrative descriptions, so that all members of the audience benefit. As with any presentation, its duration should be limited to a reasonable timescale of one or two hours. This means that there may not be time to present all the proposals. The presentation should identify the best twenty or so proposals, and should use these to promote an enthusiastic review of the remaining proposals when they are submitted in writing.

The purpose of the presentation, as stated, is to communicate an *understanding* of the proposals, and not to decide on their acceptability. The disposition of the proposals should be deferred until after the design team and decision makers have had a chance to review the detailed backup to the proposals. The VMTC should, therefore, steer the attendees away from discussing, in detail, the various pros and cons of the proposals. He should concentrate discussion instead on clarifying the audience's understanding of the individual VM proposals being presented, so that the time for presentation may be most effectively spent. The correct time to discuss the pros and cons of the proposals is during an implementation meeting which is conducted in the Post-study phase, described in Chapter 9.

8.2   Establishing a Good Atmosphere

It is useful to establish a friendly atmosphere for the presentation. The atmosphere may be enhanced by providing some form of hospitality, such as tea and biscuits. It is also necessary for the VMTC to exercise good human relations judgement, particularly with regard to the design team. The members of the original design team may be somewhat nervous about the results of the study, particularly where they have not experienced a VM study before. The VMTC should be empathetic with the design team members' position and ensure that it is fully understood that without a design in the first place the VM team would have no basis upon which to put forward proposals. The VM study should be seen as a helpful process and not as a critique or attack on the original design, which in all likelihood was good and involved an extensive amount of work and effort on the part of the design team. The VMTC may thus generate a positive atmosphere by first recognising and complementing the design team for the good work they have already completed, and by imploring them to scrutinise the proposals put forward by the VM team to ensure that all pertinent considerations have been considered. Professional courtesy should be maintained at all times by the VMTC. This courtesy may mean that obvious errors identified during the evaluation phase will be disclosed privately to the designers, and that the design team is forewarned of the proposals that are to be put forward so that they are not unduly surprised during the presentation.

8.3   Agenda

A typical agenda is set out in Working Document 8.1. As seen from this agenda, the presentation should start with a general introduction which describes the subject project under study and the scope of the VM review. This description will include details of the major constraints on the project, as well as details of any limitations placed on the VM team relative to areas of the project open for review.

The intent of the presentation as a means for communication rather than for decision making should be explained, to avoid a shift in emphasis towards implementation. Finally, the opening of this session should include introductions of the presentation attendees and the VM team.

Having conducted the general introductions, it is usually worthwhile to describe the procedure applied by the VM team in analysing the project. This description helps to establish that the exercise was not merely one of cost

Working Document 8.1 Typical oral presentation agenda

INTRODUCTION
Subject and scope of study
Intent of presentation
Introductions

VM PROCEDURE APPLIED
Study duration and location
Study participants
Stages of the job plan
Summary of proposals

DESCRIPTION OF PROPOSALS

QUESTIONS AND ANSWERS

POST-STUDY ACTIVITIES

SUMMATION

---

cutting, but was an effort aimed at *improving* the project. The study duration and location may be noted, and the various part time study participants, such as original design team members and user representatives, may be identified and thanked for their assistance.

The VMTC should then describe how the VM job plan was implemented. Initially the Information phase will be described and project cost models and function analysis models may be displayed to show how the VM team selected areas of the project to focus upon. Description of the Creative phase may merely entail a brief summary of the creative technique(s) applied, as well as identification of the number of ideas generated. The methodology applied during the Evaluation phase should then be described along with a portrayal of the manner in which the client organisation's objectives were considered in this process.

Discussion of the Development phase will describe the number of proposals actually developed, and the degree of supporting backup that will be available for review. At this point the VMTC should hand out a summary of proposals, excerpts of which are included in the Case Studies in Chapter 13 (see Working Document 13.12).

Having described the procedure applied, the presentation will then move to *discussion* of the various proposals. Until this stage the VMTC will probably have conducted the presentation. For the description of the proposals, however, it may be better for the individual VM team members to describe the proposals pertaining to their respective disciplines. The proposals should be presented in a salesman-like fashion. Rather than merely discussing the bare facts, attention should be paid to *why* the proposal should be implemented.

The benefits in terms of life cycle cost or project improvements should be stressed, together with a discussion of how any *disadvantages* may be overcome. Other issues pertinent to the attendees should also be addressed, such as the impact of implementation on the project schedule and design activities. Questions relating to understanding of the proposals should be encouraged, however, as previously stated, undue discussion as to whether or not a proposal should be accepted should be discouraged until a detailed review of the proposals by the decision makers has occurred.

Finally the presentation should conclude with a discussion of post-study activities required from various parties. An implementation meeting should be scheduled fairly shortly after the study so that delay consequences are minimised.

8.4   Presentation Skills

Presentation skills are important for communicating the correct message. While it is not the intention to describe presentation skills in depth here, it is important to understand some of the basics which will enhance an oral presentation.

Preparation

It has been said 'competence breeds confidence'. For those who are inclined toward nervousness when giving a presentation, preparedness is probably the best way to overcome such feelings. The VMTC should prepare at least a presentation outline during the study so that the actual presentation may be provided in an organised fashion. Organisation, preparation and, if there is time available, practice, can make the difference between a mediocre, dull presentation and one that inspires the attendees to agree with the recommendations and proposals.

Visual Aids

Another well-known saying is that 'a picture speaks a thousand words'. Visual aids such as overhead projections of cost model graphs and so on, may thus assist fast, effective communication of main issues. Such aids should only be used, however, where in congruence with the presentation content. The rule for overhead projections or flip chart presentations is to keep the content *simple*. If text is included, it should be limited to five or six lines of bullet points if clarity is to be achieved.

Where flip charts are used, the pages should be prepared prior to the presentation so that the presenter can merely turn the pages while talking rather than turning his back to the audience and writing.

Body Language

Body language should also be congruent with the message of the presentation. Gesticulation should reinforce a perception of conviction and belief in proposals presented and nervous actions, such as fiddling with pens, should be avoided. Eye contact should be shared between all members of the audience to display confidence, and to show that all attendees are involved and are important to the presenter.

9 Post-study Phase

9.1 Introduction

Completion of the VM study does not mean that the VM process has reached a conclusion. There are a number of essential *post-study* activities that must be carried out in order to realise the maximum benefits of the VM study. The primary focus of these activities is to ensure that feasible, advantageous proposals are actually *implemented*. The final benefit that accrues from the VM study is derived only from those proposals that are implemented and incorporated into the project strategy or design. If there is a poor implementation rate, the VM study may be considered a failure, even though numerous reasonable and advantageous proposals were generated during the study phase. The post-study activities, therefore, centre around achieving satisfactory implementation procedures to assure that good proposals are not disregarded. In addition, the post-study phase provides an opportunity to identify and collate *lessons learned*, which may be used to improve future VM studies.

The post-study phase may be considered under the following three sub phases, which will each be described in this chapter:

- Report preparation and review phase
- Implementation phase
- Follow up phase

9.2 Report Preparation and Review Phase

Introduction

The period immediately following the VM study will typically be taken up in preparing a *written report* on the study findings. A formal report serves to focus attention on the VM study, and therefore ensures that the results will not be dismissed in a casual manner.

The initial report after the study is often known as the *Preliminary Report*, as it precedes the implementation phase during which it is decided which proposals shall actually be incorporated into the project design. The report produced following the implementation phase is often termed the *Final VM Report*. Usually the only difference between these reports is that the Final Report will contain a section describing the *disposition* of the proposals, and possibly a narrative on the *lessons learned* during the VM process.

146

Obviously the scope and extent of these reports varies considerably between different VM studies, owing to the diversity of client's requirements and needs and the different stages at which the study is undertaken. There are, however, certain contents which are typically included in VM reports as well as bare essentials that should, in the authors' opinions, be included in even the most brief report. The typical contents of reports of varying comprehensiveness are shown in Working Document 9.1. These range from brief reports, which contain only essential information, to comprehensive reports which describe the entire VM process and its results. The various contents listed in Working Document 9.1 which may appear as sections in the reports are now briefly described.

Typical report contents

Executive summary   Senior management representatives in an organisation do not often have time to read and review every piece of paper that crosses their desk. They will benefit greatly from the presentation of complex issues in a compact, easy to digest, format – in other words 'in a nutshell'. An executive summary should fulfill this need and should present the most important aspects of the VM study in a concise report section that comprises only one or two pages. Since it is usually senior management who finally determine the disposition of the VM proposals, it is important to keep them informed by meeting their needs for *succinct information*.

Working Document 9.1   Typical report contents

BRIEF REPORT (minimum contents)	STANDARD REPORT	COMPREHENSIVE REPORT
Preliminary VM Report: • Executive Summary • Summary of VM Proposals • Individual VM proposals and design suggestions • List of VM team members	As Brief Report plus: • Project description • Relevant VM team comments • Function analysis forms • Ideas listing/rating forms • Copy of cost estimate • List of design documents reviewed during the study	As Standard Report plus: • Introduction • Description of VM methodology applied
Final VM Report: As above plus: • Disposition of VM proposals	As above plus: • Disposition of VM proposals • Lessons learned	As above plus: • Disposition of VM proposals • Lessons learned

The typical contents of an executive summary may include:

* Objectives of VM study
* Dates and locations of meetings together with lists of attendees
* Dates and location of the VM study
* List of VM team members and their affiliations
* A broad description of the study results e.g number of proposals, potential savings and so on
* Highlights of the study i.e. a brief description of the major proposals or concerns which arose during the study
* A brief description of the next steps to be taken in the VM process

Summary of VM proposals   This is probably the most important section in the VM report, being the section that most people review first, and possibly being the only one that some people ever look at.

The summary presents brief descriptions of the *proposals*, together with their associated *cost implications*, in an *orderly* sequence, e.g. discipline by discipline. An excerpt from a typical summary of proposals is shown in Working Document 13.7.

Some practitioners total the potential savings by totalling the relevant columns on the summary. Such totals can, however, be very misleading as there will often be a number of proposals which are mutually exclusive. Even when the total is reduced to account for the mutual exclusivity of certain proposals, the authors still do not believe the practice to be a good one. This is because it is rare that every VM proposal will be implemented. Indeed an implementation rate of 50% may be indicative of a successful VM study. The reason for this is that VM proposals often involve *trade-offs*, which can be subjective, involving individual preferences and dispositions. In order to achieve 100% acceptance of all the VM proposals, the VM team would have to be in 'perfect harmony' with the decision makers involved in determining the disposition of each VM proposal, which is a highly unlikely situation. To illustrate savings that could be achieved with 100% acceptance of proposals in effect makes a promise that is virtually impossible to fulfil. Rather than implying a promise with a tally of all the potential cost reductions, it is better to allow the decision makers to make their own estimation of potential savings by reviewing the summary of proposals and forming their own opinions as to which proposals might in fact be suitable for implementation.

Individual VM proposals and design suggestions   Each and every proposal developed during the VM study should be included in the report. The format and content of a proposal is described in Chapter 7.

List of VM team members   It is important to include a list of VM team members in order to illustrate that the VM study was conducted by an authoritative body. *Contact details* for each member are often provided so that the report recipients may communicate directly with the appropriate team members regarding any questions.

Project description   This will normally describe the project objectives, constraints, stage of design and so on. It is particularly useful for individuals who are unfamiliar with the project and acts as an excellent reference if projects need to be *reviewed* in future years.

List of design documents reviewed during the study   This records the *level of detail* available to the team at the time of the study. In addition to the usual list of drawings, etc. it should also include any *supplemental information* received from the client, such as utility rates, etc.

Copy of cost estimate   This should be the estimate used by the VM team during the study. Incorporating it, will, therefore, provide a ready reference to the basis for the *cost calculations* associated with each proposal.

Relevant VM team comments   While individual proposals cover discrete areas of potential improvement, the VM team often forms more general opinions and impressions of the project as a whole when conducting a study. For example, the VM team may consider that the project strategy is misaligned with the stated objectives. It is often worthwhile to describe broad subjective impressions such as these in a separate section of the report because they may have a positive influence on the *future direction* of the project, but they are unlikely to be communicated clearly by individual proposals.

Function analysis forms   Since function analysis is a key element of a VM study, the results of such an analysis should be included in the report. Care should be exercised to explain how this analysis is related to the aims and results of the VM study to avoid confusion amongst the report recipients. This may be covered with a brief narrative in the *function analysis section* of the report.

Idea list/rating forms   A typical idea list/rating form is illustrated in Working Document 5.1. It is useful to incorporate these forms to identify the full extent of ideas considered versus those that were ultimately selected for development. Furthermore, some ideas on the list, that were not developed during the study due to a lack of time, might be valuable if budgetary problems occur later in the project. As mentioned in the Evaluation phase, these undeveloped proposals may provide a ready source of *cost reduction ideas* which may be implemented to prevent budget overruns.

VM study methodology This section provides a description of the VM methodology that was applied, commencing with pre-study activities followed by details of each step in the job plan, and finally, a summation of post-study activities. It may also include the VM *study agenda*. The inclusion of this description is often useful in that it illustrates that the study was conducted in a manner conducive to project improvement and the removal of unnecessary cost, as opposed to cost cutting achieved by cheapening the project.

9.3 Implementation Phase

Introduction

It does not necessarily follow that a productive VM study which yields many substantive proposals will result in the incorporation of those proposals into the project strategy or design. Improving the probability of such an occurrence requires careful forethought and planning. A plan for closing out a VM study during the post-study phase is therefore an essential ingredient for the successful application of VM. This plan should be developed by the client organisation's VM project manager, and should provide solutions which overcome the hindrance of the implementation of good, advantageous proposals.

Potential Hindrances

While it is difficult to identify all potential hindrances to implementation there are some which occur relatively frequently, the most common of which are now described.

Opposition by the design team When an external VM team has been used there are many reasons why the design team might be inclined to put up barriers against the implementation of certain VM proposals. Some reasons are based on objective reasoning regarding disadvantages of various proposals and, therefore, are valid. Others are less valid and may be based on very subjective reasoning. Designers, quite naturally, can be very committed to their personally developed designs and may, therefore, tend to resist any adaptations which would materially change their concept. Another subjective reason for rejection, or resistance, may simply be due to a feeling that acceptance of the VM proposals will, in some way, imply a *criticism* of their work. Practical reasons may also be behind resistance, such as a situation whereby implementation of a VM proposal will require some redesign for which the client is unwilling to provide additional payment.

Unwillingness by the user to re-examine criteria Sometimes an end user will prescribe certain criteria for which they have no valid or practical justification. Such criteria may result from the user's *habit*, or *culture*, or may derive from some *political* motive. Whatever the reason, there are occasions when end users can be quite obstinate about retaining design elements that are suboptimal.

Programming concerns Incorporation of some VM proposals may be disruptive to a project's programme. Whilst this is, on occasion, a valid reason for rejection, it can also be a good cover for an invalid reason or any unjustified opposition.

Disagreement among parties If all parties are in disagreement regarding some or all of the contents of a particular VM proposal, rejection can be an all too easy answer to the problem.

Lack of motivation In the absence of an individual with the responsibility to supervise the implementation of good VM proposals, it is likely that the only proposals to be implemented will be those that do not cause 'too much' difficulty. In circumstances where VM is imposed on organisations by mandatory requirement, the parties will often just go through the motions without a great incentive to obtain good results from VM studies.

An organisation may overcome the hindrances noted above by appointing a VM *project manager* who is aware of, and thus guards against, the potential for unjustified rejection of proposals. The VM project manager is usually a different individual from the VMTC, and is involved with the overall supervision of an organisation's activities rather than running individual studies.

The Implementation Process

The objective of the implementation process is to determine the *final disposition* of each of the VM proposals developed during the study phase. This objective may be satisfactorily realised by following a two step procedure.

First, having allowed the various parties involved in the decision process sufficient time to review the preliminary VM report, they should be requested to submit their *initial response* to the VM proposals. This response should be in writing and should list, for each VM proposal, one of three optional responses:

- Accepted
- Rejected
- Further study required.

While only a one word response is sufficient for the accepted proposals, it is good practice to require the parties to provide a brief explanation for proposals which they want rejected or deferred for further study. Requesting the various parties to submit their reasons for rejection in writing generally deters them from dismissing a proposal on invalid grounds: very few individuals are willing to commit unjustifiable or poor reasoning to paper.

Upon receipt of the responses the VM project manager should tabulate the results and review the reasons behind the rejection of proposals, or requirements for further study and determine their validity. Often the various parties will differ in their responses. These differences may be reconciled in the second step in the implementation process which is the *implementation meeting*.

The implementation meeting should be attended by all interested parties. Attendees should include the organisation's decision makers, design team representatives and VM team representatives. It is also good to involve an individual from senior management where possible, as this will tend to encourage an effective and productive meeting.

The purpose of the implementation meeting is to resolve any differences of opinion regarding the disposition of proposals so as to finalise their disposition. Any proposals listed as rejected in the parties' written responses should be discussed. By having the appropriate VM team members present, any misconceptions evident in the responses may be corrected. Those proposals listed for further study should also be discussed in detail, after which decisions will be sought. As far as possible decisions are obtained regarding which proposals should be accepted, left for further study as the design progresses, or rejected. Where such agreement is not possible, the proposal may be recorded as an open item which requires some further action or study prior to determination of its final disposition.

9.4   Follow Up Phase

Any proposals left open after the implementation meeting should be pursued to obtain closure in the Follow up phase.

Another follow up activity that may be useful is the preparation of a brief report on the *lessons learned* from the VM study. This report should be issued to parties who will be involved with future VM studies, so that they may benefit from any insight gained from the previous VM activities. Future VM studies may also benefit from a review of previous VM proposals so it may be worthwhile to enter the results of each study into a central database.

While lessons may be derived from the VM study itself, a more detailed measurement of the *benefits* of the VM study may be made during a *post-occupancy evaluation review*. Such a review should, where relevant, describe the impact of VM on the completed facility. This information will again provide useful feedback for further studies.

9.5 Improving VM Results

As emphasised in previous chapters, it is widely agreed that the involvement of senior management in the VM programme is a most essential ingredient for successful VM studies. The presence of senior management will often bring out the best in those involved in the VM process and, therefore, will be likely to improve results, especially during the post-study phase.

Another potential mechanism by which organisational members' participation in VM may be improved is by making the performance of employees in the VM process an element in the periodic *employee evaluation process*. When employees are aware that performance ratings may be influenced by their participation in VM activities, they may well be inclined to put more effort and dedication into this area of the business, which is likely to lead to an overall improvement in VM results.

PART III

Other VM Issues

10 Initiating a VM Programme

10.1 Introduction

An extensive study of VM programmes in construction around the USA, which was conducted by one of the authors, revealed that they have had a very checquered history – many have succeeded, but some have failed.

The study provided many lessons and conclusions. The VM unit must be located in some part of the organisation which has *authority*. Funding for a small in-house staff is usually a must and the ability to bring in qualified value specialists, as well as some outside experts, is also a must. In addition, it is highly desirable to have the ability to bring in technical team members when it is difficult or impractical to borrow appropriate in-house engineers, architects, and estimators for VM studies.

In addition to the above, care should be taken to select suitable *projects* for VM. It is probably impractical to use VM on every project. When selecting projects, especially at the start of a new VM programme, those projects with a known need or problem should be given priority.

VM produces the best results when its aim is to satisfy all project needs, and not just to focus on cost reduction. The aim is to develop a partnership among those responsible for design, operations and cost management, and to get everyone working together towards one goal – the *best project for the funds available*. In VM, this is accomplished by bringing together everyone involved in a project, in the same room, at the same time, to hear and understand each other's objectives for the project. Then, using the VM technique of function analysis, the parties agree on a complete list of objectives, or functions, against which every aspect of the design will be measured.

10.2 Setting the VM Programme's Objectives

As a first step in the design of a new VM programme, its *objective* must be selected. The goals of a VM programme should be positive objectives which derive directly from the objectives of the overall organisation. A common mistake in setting up a VM programme is to set goals which by their very nature are *negative objectives*.

Unfortunately, a very typical aim when VM programmes are started is simple cost cutting. There is nothing wrong with identifying and eliminating unnecessary costs in order to make the money saved available for more beneficial uses. There is also nothing wrong with finding ways to bring a project cost back to a level which is within available funding, and thereby permit it to proceed without the usual delays which occur when a funding problem is discovered. However, using VM simply as a means to cut cost, just for the sake of cutting cost with no beneficial end in mind, is a negative activity.

Another aim, although it is not usually acknowledged as such, is to use VM as a *weapon*. This may take a variety of forms depending on the part of the organisation which controls the VM programme. VM can be used as a means to attack the end user's inflated brief request, or the designer's grandiose solution, or the project manager's uneconomical short cuts for keeping the project on schedule. While eliminating unnecessary elements of the brief, or scaling back a design to an appropriate solution, or avoiding costly short cuts are desirable goals, using VM as a weapon to overpower the end user, or to embarrass the designer, or to attack the project manager is both unnecessary and counterproductive.

VM is a powerful tool. It should be used only for *positive* purposes. Using it as a vindictive weapon is an abuse of its power, and in the long run such abuses will backfire on the VM programme because as time passes more and more enemies of the VM programme will be developed. These enemies will be ready and waiting to blame VM every time a problem develops in a project which can somehow be related back to a VM proposal. This can eventually lead to a constant barrage of criticism with which the organisation will be forced to deal. An expected result would be to get rid of the troublesome VM programme altogether, or at least to remove its teeth.

Such problems are totally unnecessary and can be avoided by always aiming for positive objectives. When a VM programme clearly demonstrates that all its efforts are being directed strictly towards helping to achieve the organisation's overall goals, and it is not using VM in a vindictive way, top management will have no patience with unwarranted criticism of VM, and any criticism will tend to backfire on the critics. When you stay on the side of the angels it is much easier to stay out of harm's way.

Different parts of an organisation have somewhat different objectives which are, to some extent, in conflict with one another. The design group is focused on the quality of its designs. Project management tends to emphasise the project programme. The construction division wants uncomplicated construction, and the finance group is primarily concerned with costs. However, one part of an organisation, top management, must be concerned with all of these areas, and they must direct their efforts toward achieving the optimum balance among them. Achieving this objective is essential to achieving the overall goals of the organisation, and this is the objective VM should pursue.

10.3   Using VM to Help Satisfy the Organisation's Needs

VM is most effective when it is designed to answer the organisation's needs and existing problems. As top management must view projects from an overall perspective, they need to pursue ways to enhance their ability to make independent assessments of proposed new projects and their estimates of cost.

Major capital projects involve many areas of expertise, such as specialised planners and architects and engineers from many disciplines. Since no one in top management can be expert in all of these areas, his or her review is disadvantaged. To counter this, a VM programme should be structured to provide the ability to bring in all needed experts for just the short time that they are needed. The aim should be to provide top management with authoritative evaluations of every important project aspect, as well as independent evaluations of the estimates for both capital and future operating costs.

A VM programme should also be structured to deal with management's other problem relative to special projects – insufficient review time. Management's time is spread too thin. A large percentage of it is spent on day-to-day activities with little time left for in depth analysis. Since special projects require even more time, the VM unit should support management by relieving them of this problem.

VM should be used as a means to provide management with authoritative evaluations of underlying issues involved in proposed project briefs or designs, and their related capital and operating costs. It should seek to identify potential problems early, when it is still possible to implement changes easily, instead of having to deal with the problems after they occur. It should also provide management with the information it needs to make informed decisions. In addition, VM can provide acceptable cost reductions, since there is no such thing as a perfect scope or a perfect design, and funds saved by eliminating unnecessary cost can always find a home.

10.4   Involving Top Management

The function of top management is to ensure that the organisation's *objectives are met*, and their efforts are measured by how well they achieve this function. It follows that VM will help to make management look good when it is instrumental in assisting them to achieve these objectives. However, in order to take credit for the VM unit's success, management should appear to own the VM programme, which will require their involvement. While management's involvement is highly desirable, it should be kept to a minimum so as not to add to their workload.

The VM unit is normally created to alleviate and solve problems, therefore it should not present management with more problems – it should, rather, present them with solutions. The VM unit should keep management informed as to how it is attending to their concerns, and only seek management's guidance on essential issues. Such issues would include management's guidance regarding strategic business objectives, and on occasion their involvement to resolve problems that are beyond the VM unit's control.

Specific VM activities where management's involvement would be desirable and appropriate could include:

- Review of the *list of projects* selected by the VM unit for study
- Review of periodic VM *progress reports* on the projects in the VM programme
- Review of the *action plan* for individual VM projects, including the areas on which the VM team will be directed to focus their attention, the in-house personnel who will participate, or the types of outside experts who will be needed
- A brief talk with the VM team, at the beginning of the workshop, to demonstrate management's support for the VM effort and to lay out *overall objectives* and the organisation's *expectations* from the VM effort
- Attendance at the VM team's presentation of the *proposals* it developed during the VM study
- Review of the results of *implementation meetings* at which the disposition of individual VM proposals were decided
- Review of progress reports relative to activities under way to achieve *closure* on any open items for which a final disposition was not decided at the implementation meeting
- Final decision on *open items* when involved parties cannot reach agreement.

10.5   Use of External Consultants

Team Members

It is reasonably common practice to use in-house personnel to staff VM teams. This approach can be effective if prudently implemented. The important consideration is to use at least some people who were not involved in the project, owing to a need for objectivity. However, hiring external professionals to staff VM teams has a number of advantages over using only in-house staff. Using in-house staff presents a variety of problems which do not have to be dealt with when external professionals are used.

The first problem has to do with the availability of individuals who would be best suited to participate in the study. The level of success of a VM study is directly proportional to the quality of the VM team members. Therefore, getting the organisation's best people for each slot on the VM team is very important. Unfortunately, an organisation's best people always have too much to do already, and getting them away from their regular duties can be difficult, if not impossible. The result is that less qualified individuals may be the only ones who can be spared for special assignments.

A different problem might be the lack of needed experts for particular important areas of the VM study because the organisation does not have a need for those types of experts for regular business operations. With this problem, there are only two alternatives, either do without or bring in an outside expert.

Another problem is that in-house personnel are often groomed to conform to the organisation's standard ways of doing things. As a result, they may tend to be less inclined to explore alternatives during a VM study.

The use of external team members has the advantage of permitting the organisation to get exactly those experts who are needed, at precisely the point in time when their services will be needed, and for only the few days the VM workshop is in session. Of course, the disadvantage of using external team members is that this adds cost to the VM study. While it can be argued that the investment will almost always pay for itself many times over, if the needed funds are simply not available, this argument is mute.

One solution is to compromise and use a *mixed team*. In-house personnel can be used to staff most of the VM team while external experts are used for areas where the needed type of expertise is not available within the organisation, or for an important area of the study where an impartial second perspective could be most valuable.

VMTCs or Facilitators

Again, it is reasonably common practice for organisations to use in-house personnel to act as VMTCs and facilitate their VM studies. While such an approach may be satisfactory, problems can occur, especially during periods of peak workload. The tendency is to deal with such peaks by taking short cuts on important parts of the VM process. A typical short cut may be to reduce the reports to a bare minimum. While this practise will not necessarily have harmful effects in the short run, it may do so in the long run. Brevity of reports may reduce accountability and allow other potentially harmful short cuts to go unnoticed.

There are a number of potential advantages associated with using external VM consultants, either to supplement in-house staff or to facilitate all the organisation's VM studies. VM consultants can generally be expected to have broad experience of applying VM to many different types of projects which will enable them to introduce considerations that may not have been generated by in-house staff. In addition, the *independence* of an external consultant should reduce any problems caused by organisational prejudices or politics. The use of external consultants shall also enable an organisation to cope with *fluctuations in demand* for VM studies in a cost efficient manner by only employing their services when actually needed.

Selection of External Consultants

Since the results of a VM study usually result in significant project cost savings which far outweigh the costs of the study, it may not be prudent to base external consultant selections heavily on fee considerations.

As explained earlier, the quality of the VM team structure and content acts as a major determinant of the level of results that will be achieved from a VM study. While high calibre VM consultants and team members may result in higher study costs, their involvement is likely to result in significantly better study results. The marginally higher study cost would thus, usually, represent an excellent return on investment.

For this reason, a fairly common approach to external consultant selection for VM is to seek *separate technical proposals* and *cost tenders* from prospective consultants. When the tender evaluation process is undertaken only the technical proposals will initially be considered in the selection of the preferred consultant. Where a VM consultant is providing both the facilitator and team members, the evaluation may consider such issues as:

- Qualifications of the individuals proposed, in terms of training, credentials and experience
- Firm's track record, in terms of previous results and experience on similar project types
- Proposed methodology, in terms of whether authentic VM practices will be followed; how well the specific requirements of the project are understood; the appropriateness of the manpower allocation, and so on
- Organisation, in terms of the team structure, the depth of support and management of the provision of services.

Generally the evaluators will only open the cost tender of the consultant judged to be most suitable from the technical proposal. Only if they cannot reach a negotiated agreement with that consultant will the next most preferred proposer's cost tender be opened.

While other methods of selection are available, this practice very effectively deals with the need to place priority on quality, as opposed merely to cost.

10.6   Resources

A VM programme does require an investment, but it is minimal in comparison to the return it produces. Funds should be made available to establish a small, dedicated, technical staff to manage and administer the programme and to provide funds for the VM consultants or any experts who might be needed to conduct the VM studies. Usually, such funding can be part of the project capital budget and need not be included in an organisation's operating budget.

10.7 The VM Unit

Introduction

Even when external consultants are used to provide VM team facilitators and members, it is often still necessary to have organisational personnel dedicated to the VM programme on a full-time basis. This unit will be staffed by VM project managers who take responsibility for supervising the whole VM process, as opposed to VMTCs who are normally only involved in the more technical VM activities which revolve mainly around the VM study itself.

Where to Locate the VM Unit

VM programmes succeed or fail depending on where they are *installed* in an organisation. Since VM is more likely to succeed when it is located in a department which has an expressed need for it, it should be established in some department which is concerned with projects from an overall perspective, including both improved quality and cost management.

Another consideration is that a VM unit needs to be backed up by the authority of a high level executive. VM programmes cannot succeed when they are established in an environment which is not conducive to success. To succeed, the programme's needs must be met. The first need is *authority*: the programme must have support from some part of top management, and it must satisfy some need of that part of management.

VM programmes fail when they are installed in a department as a response to a mandate requiring VM, if the department neither perceives a need for it nor has a commitment to its success.

VM programmes also fail when they are located in a department which has a *conflicting interest*. This can result in the VM reviews being prevented from examining every aspect of the projects under study. Unfortunately, this is a usual problem when VM is located under the aegis of a design department. Since the design department produced the designs which are the subjects of the VM reviews, their tendency is to protect their work by restricting the scope of the reviews. When VM is part of a design department, the department tends to try to prevent the study from going into important areas which really need to be examined objectively. Usually this is because they do not want to reopen those aspects of the design, but sometimes they simply do not want outsiders looking over their shoulders at decisions that have been made.

Role of the VM Project Manager

Having a *full-time staff* to manage the VM programme is another key element of success. It might seem that the supervision of VM studies could be performed by a VM project manager on a part-time basis. It is true that participation in VM workshops uses only a small percentage of a VM project manager's time. However, a much greater share of his time must be devoted to other activities. These activities include tracking the progress of candidate projects, preparing for workshops and, after they are completed, the most difficult task of closing out the study.

While the cost of VM is minimal with respect to total project costs, VM studies do cost money. To get maximum benefits from this investment careful preparations are necessary. The project must be *researched* to identify issues and areas of concern. The *team structure* must be shaped so that it will be fully equipped to deal with these issues and concerns. If an outside VM consultant is used, the VM project manager may have to work with the value specialist to identify candidates for each position on the VM team, and to review their qualifications. After the team structure is established, the participation time for each team member must be worked out, and contract details must be finalised.

With the contract in place, the VM project manager must start the *workshop preparations*. Representatives of each department or organisation who should participate must be contacted well in advance in order for them to reserve the time when they will be needed. Documents and other information must be collected and reviewed to determine if the total material is sufficient for a good study. If it is not, the additional material needed must be pursued and obtained. The VM project manager should also prepare a detailed scope for the VM team, which highlights the areas where the team will be required to focus its efforts during the workshop, and lists any appropriate constraints, e.g. whether or not they should challenge a given criterion.

Finally, the VM project manager should organise an orientation meeting and site visit before the workshop to make sure that all is in order, and that everyone involved is familiar with the project's main elements and issues. The overall objective of these *pre-study activities* is to have everything ready and together so that when the appropriate time for the study arrives it can commence without delay, with the team knowing exactly what they should do, and having everything they will need to do the job.

During the workshop, the project manager should be in attendance on a full-time basis in order to be completely familiar with each of the VM proposals, including the discussions which led up to them. It is important for the project manager to have this knowledge because it provides the link between the VM team and the organisation when the VM team disbands. This is especially important when the VM team includes outside experts. Without the VM project manager's knowledge, much *background information* will be lost.

After the VM workshop, the project manager's efforts focus on trying to *complete* the study. When the completed VM report is distributed to all interested parties, the project manager should obtain everyone's responses. When received, he may schedule an implementation meeting. The purpose of this meeting is to get agreement with respect to the disposition of each VM proposal. The group must determine which VM proposals are to be implemented, which are to be rejected, which require further study during the next project development phase, and which will remain open after the meeting because parties cannot reach agreement. These results must then be recorded and distributed to all involved parties.

The next step is to try to reach *closure* on the open proposals. Quite often this is the most difficult task. A proposed dispute resolution process is outlined below. This too would consume part of the project manager's time.

Selecting Staff

Managing a VM programme or individual VM studies requires the skills which are basic for most managers. The individual should be an intelligent self-starter. He or she should have natural leadership qualities and be a good communicator, both verbally and in writing. He should also have the courage to stand up and challenge the status quo.

In addition to the above basic personal qualities, the individual should have relevant training and/or experience. Prior cost management training is a definite plus. Another plus would be a broad knowledge of the organisation's particular areas of business and, more particularly, the structure and procedures of the organisation itself.

10.8   The VM Steering Committee

There are many reasons for using VM but there is one which should be highlighted. Every design reflects the results of *competition* among various aspects of a project, such as quality, required functions, programme and cost. In a perfect design all aspects would be provided for to an appropriate degree. Unfortunately, designs are rarely perfect. A common condition is that one of the aspects is overemphasised and one or more of the other aspects are compromised.

As stated above, the objective of the VM programme should be to help meet overall organisation goals, not the goals of one department. Thus, no one department, including the VM unit's parent department, should be able to dominate the programme and focus the VM efforts primarily on its concerns. To ensure that the VM programme's focus is on all project aspects, an *inter-departmental steering committee* should be established. The committee meetings should serve to ensure that each department understands the impact of its decisions on other departments, on the project as a whole, and on the total organisation.

The committee, at minimum, will include representatives from the design department, the relevant operating department and the financial department. Representatives from other departments may also be included, as appropriate. The committee should participate in most of the important functions of the VM programme, including study planning and, most important, in deciding the *disposition* of each proposal developed by the VM team. The representatives will also be expected to act as liaisons between the VM Unit and their respective departments.

Another important function of the committee members will be to bring the resources of their respective departments to the VM efforts. For example, the operating units can help determine the types of experts needed for particular studies and identify the best people in those fields. The design department can support the VM unit in the selection and hiring of subconsultants, and they can also make their existing contracting processes available for the VM Unit's contracts.

In summary, the objective of this committee is to get everyone in the same boat, all rowing in the same direction.

10.9   The Implementation Process

Closing out a VM study can be the single most problematic task in VM. It should be understood that different members of an organisation see VM proposals from entirely different perspectives. Consequently, they will differ on whether or not specific VM proposals should be implemented. In order to deal with this situation a *structured implementation process* is a must. Without one, indecision will reign and good VM proposals can easily wither and die. Chapter 9 deals with this subject in detail.

10.10   The Dispute Resolution Process

A dispute resolution process should be established so that if, after a VM implementation meeting all interested parties have not reached agreement on a VM proposal, a mechanism is in place to break the impasse. The first step in the process would be to try to settle the issue on an informal basis. If that does not produce resolution, the matter would be referred to the VM Steering Committee. Next it would go to the department heads. Then, if the matter was still unresolved, the VM unit would prepare a brief memo to the designated senior management executive requesting a final decision. This memo would detail the differing departments' positions. Their concurrence in the statements of their positions should be obtained before forwarding the memo.

To avoid undue delay, a programme should be developed allowing a maximum period from the date of the implementation meeting to the forwarding of the memo to the senior management executive.

10.11   The Work Plan

At the outset, projects selected for VM reviews should be fairly large or they should exhibit some *need* – a cost problem, unusual public sensitivity, a concern about future operating costs, or some other problem which calls for special attention. Then the type of study which will lead off the VM programme must be selected. While many organisations start their programme with VE studies, the authors consider that it is often preferable to commence with a *VP study*. This is because a VP study can be expected to result in impressive proposals which can be easily appreciated and implemented without added cost.

Having impressed the organisation with an initial study, a VM programme may be established which requires a series of VM studies to be applied during the course of each appropriate project. This series may include an initial strategic VP study (explained in Chapter 11) together with subsequent VP and VE studies.

The points at which studies are undertaken will obviously vary by client and project type, etc. Working Document 10.1 shows a typical VM study programme for building type projects.

10.12   Overcoming Handicaps

There are many handicaps which can be imposed on a VM effort. Sometimes the process can be cut short by changing or dropping critical parts. The process can also be handicapped by going in the opposite direction – extending it and changing it into an ongoing, piecemeal exercise. In either case the result is the same. It is no longer authentic VM: it is something similar, but it is considerably less effective due to the change.

The VM unit needs to be insulated from the usual sources of handicaps. When it is located as part of top management this is not a problem, because top management has no reason to want to handicap the VM process.

10.13   VM Orientation

At the initiation of the VM programme some *familiarisation seminars* should be scheduled to acquaint staff involved with VM as to what it is all about, and how it is to be implemented. There should be one seminar for involved

Working Document 10.1   Typical VM study programme for building-type projects

VALUE MANAGEMENT

VALUE PLANNING (Strategic)	VALUE ENGINEERING	VALUE ANALYSIS

RIBA PLAN OF WORK	BRIEFING		SKETCH PLANS		WORKING DRAWINGS				CONSTRUCTION	POST-CONSTRUCTION
	Inception	Feasibility	Outline Proposals	Scheme Design	Detail Design	Production Information	Bills of Quantities	Tender Action	Construction	Post-Occupancy Evaluation

department heads and some of their key staff, and another for those individuals from design, operations and budget who will be participating in the planned studies. These types of training sessions are explained in more detail in Chapter 12.

10.14   Conclusion

New VM programmes succeed when all essential ingredients are included at their outset; when the programmes are structured to deal with existing problems; and when an environment conducive to success is established. Success also requires the selection of good candidate projects but, most importantly, the programme's aim must be to achieve *value*, not simply to reduce cost.

11 Strategic VP and VM's Role in Project Management

11.1 Introduction

Whereas the main body of this book is dedicated to the fundamentals of the VM methodology, this chapter presents more advanced VM applications such as strategic VP and places VM in its context with respect to other project management activities.

11.2 Strategic VP

Many organisations are introduced to VM through initial VE studies. Often, encouraged by the results of VE, and intuitively knowing that greater results may be obtained from earlier studies, they apply VM at progressively earlier stages in the design process or project's life cycle.

The first step taken may be to apply VM at the end of the Briefing Stage. This has been described earlier in the book as a VP study. Such a VP study will, in broad terms, follow the same methodology as VE but will review '*what*' is to be built rather than '*how*' it is to be constructed, which would be the subject of later VE studies.

Having gained success in the VP studies during early design, organisations are often prompted to take a further step and introduce VM at the very earliest stages in a project's life cycle, i.e. during Inception and Feasibility stages of the RIBA plan of work. Such studies are denoted as strategic VP studies in this book (but are also sometimes also annotated as VM1). Strategic VP studies are, by virtue of the stage at which they are conducted, inherently different to the VM studies conducted at later stages.

VP and VE studies undertaken beyond the briefing stage have concrete information which can be reviewed by the VM team and built upon or improved by the proposals resulting from the study. VM at these stages is not meant to supplant the good work done by the project planners, designers or engineers, but is rather meant to supplement their work through the application of the fast and effective VM methodology. At the Feasibility stage far less concrete information will be available in normal circumstances. As such, the nature of VM activity must be modified to suit the different situation.

The major differences between a strategic VP study and later studies are its scope and its emphasis. First, the scope of the study will be far *broader* than later studies. Whereas the decision to build is often a given after the Briefing stage, at Feasibility stage such a decision is still open to question. Various alternatives to a built solution may equally meet an organisation's needs. For example, a consumer products company looking to expand its production capacity may consider the alternatives of building its own factory, leasing manufacturing space, subcontracting out production to other manufacturers, and so on. The strategic VP study should, therefore, usually consider whether a proposal to construct is, in fact, the best manner in which to meet the organisational objectives.

This difference in scope has major consequences for the structure of the team required for the VM study. It shifts the focus away from purely construction-type matters to broader business-type areas. Consequentially, business and management consultants may be equally or more valuable VM team members than construction consultants. Furthermore, it will probably benefit the study if the facilitator has a greater orientation towards business than merely construction matters.

The second major factor differentiating strategic VP from later VM is its *emphasis*. At such an early stage, the various interested parties of an organisation may have had relatively little chance to consider and discuss their respective objectives for a proposed project. Whilst VM at all stages seeks to understand the organisation's objectives through function analysis and other activities during the information stage, this may be difficult to do at such an early stage when objectives may not yet be clearly understood. Thus a major emphasis of the strategic VP study is to get *key stakeholders* together to identify their various objectives.

Broad level function analysis may be used to stimulate discussion and subsequently to 'pry' these objectives from the stakeholders. The implications of this are that all the key stakeholders should attend, or be represented, at the VM study and that proportionally a greater amount of study time will be spent on Information phase-type activities than would probably be the case for subsequent studies. Having spent due time discussing and agreeing the business objectives or 'functions' required, the Creative phase may be used, as previously intimated, to generate both alternative construction proposals as well as non-construction ideas. During the Evaluation phase, it is likely that complex comparison and rating tools such as the criteria scoring matrix described in Chapter 6 will be used as a means to assist decision making. As relatively fewer proposals of greater scope will be likely to result from these early VM studies, simpler evaluation techniques are unlikely to be appropriate. Considerable Development phase activities may be required concerning the various proposals, but these may be conducted outside the scope of the study to avoid consuming too much of the key stakeholders' time.

Due to the relatively higher order level of subject matter considered during the strategic VP, together with the fact that a number of the participants will be key stakeholders from fairly senior management positions whose time is precious, the duration of a typical study at this stage will be relatively short. Such studies may require only a day or two of direct workshop-type activity. Strategic VP thus involves validating whether a construction project is an appropriate solution for an organisation's objectives and, if so, helps key stakeholders to at least start to reconcile what functions should be performed by the facility to satisfy the objectives. It is different from later VM studies in both its scope and emphasis. These fundamental differences cause related variations in the team skills required for, and the duration of, the study.

Such studies may be harder to conduct than later studies, and the benefits may be less obvious to appreciate for those not involved with the process. For these reasons, the authors consider it to be preferable to introduce VM to an organisation via later studies. This enables organisational participants to gain a firm understanding of the basics of VM methodology before moving onto earlier, less clearly defined VM activities. In addition, the later activities will produce more obvious and measurable benefits, which will hopefully secure VM's future in the organisation.

11.3   VM and Other Project Management Activities

VM should not operate in a vacuum, but should be integrated with, or cognisant of, other important project management activities. VM's relationship with cost, programme and risk management and with procurement route decisions and constructability reviews are discussed briefly in this section.

VM and Cost Management

By this stage in the book, it should be clear that VM and cost management are quite different activities. Both are useful and necessary components of effective project management and one should not be used in lieu of the other. While VM provides authoritative, multi-disciplinary reviews at *milestone points* cost management provides ongoing control of costs *throughout the project*. Without this ongoing control it is likely that the benefits reaped from VM will either not be fully realised, or will be swamped by the cost escalation following VM activities.

There are important links between the two activities, which means that, when combined, the total combined effect is greater than the sum of the individual effects. Cost management enhances VM activities in several ways. First, it is the quantity surveyor or cost engineer who provides cost management that produces the estimates and cost data for VM studies. Good detailed cost estimates and data greatly improve the quality of VM proposals and the basis for decision making. Secondly, if there is no ongoing cost management, VM proposals selected during the implementation phase may not actually be incorporated into the design. Another possibility is that the proposals may be incorporated soon after the study but may be deleted from the design at a later stage. This may occur as part of a general wave of 'scope creep', during which additional items are continually added to the scope of work in an unchecked manner.

VM assists cost management efforts first by producing probable cost savings of 5–10% (or, on occasions, much more). Secondly, VM provides a list of ideas which, although not necessarily developed during the VM study, could provide cost reductions if necessary at a later stage in the project: if the project budget appears to be exceeded at any stage the VM report should be reviewed as a ready reference for ideas for cost reduction measures.

VM and the Project Programme

The degree of importance placed on time for project completion will vary between different client types. For example, consumer products companies are under ever-increasing pressure from the competition to shorten product-to-market cycles and their relative priority for timely construction will be high.

The level of priority given to time should be established before the VM study and addressed in a manner befitting its importance. On some occasions it may, for example, be appropriate to suggest proposals which add cost but shave significant time from the project programme. Where time is of the essence, it will be useful to have a *critical path network programme* for review during the study.

While it is often argued by opponents to VM that the process itself will delay design and thus the overall project programme, this is not necessarily so. By holding VM studies at strategic milestone points during the design process, at which there are natural breaks for normal reviews, design delays can be eliminated. In other words, if VM is made an integral part of the *overall design process*, as it should be, it will be built into the programme and properly timed. Delay, in this case, will only occur when VM uncovers a problem which must be solved before the design advances. Blaming VM for these occurrences is like blaming a fire on the person who sounded the fire alarm. In a fire, the sooner the alarm is sounded, the less the damage will be. This is also the case when VM uncovers a problem. As time goes on, the difficulty in correcting it will increase, as will the extent of the delay. VM's finding it sooner, in actuality, therefore reduces the delay that would have occurred later anyway. Furthermore, frequently VM proposals will not just produce cost savings but will also reduce the time required for construction by deleting unnecessary scope of work, or by addressing constructability issues. Such savings may significantly outweigh any delays to the design process.

VM and Project Risk Management

While systematic project risk management has been called for by academics for some years and has been practised on certain project types such as oil and gas projects, its use until recently has been fairly limited in connection with general construction. Over recent years, however, there has been a growing acceptance of the proposition that such a practice may be useful in connection with virtually all types of construction projectS.

Project risk management may be achieved through the use of a system which identifies and analyses risks and provides a mechanism by which they may be dealt with. Such a system may be enacted through a Project Risk Management Plan derived from a structured process which would include:

• Risk assessment and categorisation
• Risk analysis
• Risk response

Each of these steps are briefly described below.

Risk assessment

Risk assessment involves identifying the various risks involved with a project, and then categorising them according to their *type, impact* or *consequence*. Generally, the risks will be categorised to collate similar risks. For example, a proposed water treatment facility using a new technology may have technical risks associated with a relative lack of certainty about the performance of the new system as well as environmental risks due to the possibility of changing statutory requirements for water treatment. In this case, the categories of 'technical and 'environmental' issues may be identified amongst other risk issue categories.

Having identified and broadly categorised the risks, they may then be *qualitatively assessed* as high, medium or low risks with regard to their potential consequences. On the one extreme there may be risks which are potential 'show stoppers' that would cause major delays, cost overruns or performance shortfalls. At the other end of the spectrum would be low risk issues with fairly minor impacts on the cost, programme or performance of the project.

Having identified, categorised and qualitatively assessed the risk issues, they may then be quantitatively analysed, as now described.

Risk analysis

Risk analysis will usually consist of some form of *quantitative measurement* of the consequence of the risk issues. This analysis will allocate measurements which will more definitively describe the level of risk associated with particular risk issues. The level of analysis differs in complexity according to the nature of the project and the capabilities of those conducting the analysis. A simple form of quantitative analysis may merely comprise subjective judgement regarding the probable consequences of each risk issue. The cost and/or time consequences derived in this manner may then be totalled together to gain an impression of the level of risk in terms of most likely and maximum values.

More sophisticated analyses may involve *computerised probability analysis.* Minimum, maximum and most likely cost and time values will be established and used to produce probability curves through computerised simulation. These probability curves will provide a range of project out-turn costs and time values against their probability of occurrence as indicated in Figure 11.1. Such a risk analysis may serve to more realistically display potential project costs and programmes for decision makers, and can be of use when allocating contingencies to various project elements.

Risk response

Having assessed and analysed the various risks relating to a project then next step is to decide how these risks should be dealt with. The manner in which they are dealt with, or responded to, will depend on their probability of occurrence and potential severity of consequence.

Where risks are relatively minor in nature, they may be retained and merely borne in mind during the management of the project. Risks with more severe consequences and a relatively high probability of occurrence may be mitigated by several measures. Such measures may include *transferring* the risk in whole or part under contractual arrangements or insurance, or *modifying the project design or strategy* to reduce 'risky' elements. Severe risks with a high probability of occurrence may warrant complete avoidance by cancelling a project altogether.

Having gone through each of the preceding steps a *Risk Management Plan* document may be prepared, which will include a list of risk issues which will each have a corresponding assessment of consequences and mitigating measures. In addition, the plan may include a quantitative risk analysis which will provide the ranges of potential cost and time out-turns for the project. As the levels of risk will change over time, this plan should be continually reviewed as the project progresses, and updated as necessary.

By explicitly recognising potential future risks, a project risk management system will assist better decision making and improve the management of projects. Risks may be identified and dealt with before they turn into problems or catastrophes. Alternatively, *contingency plans* may be formulated against risk issues so that if the problem does actually occur in the future it

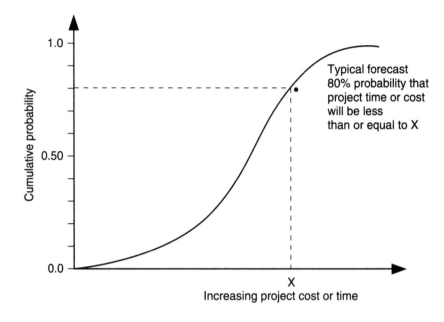

Figure 11.1   Range of time or cost out-turn forecasts from risk analysis

may be dealt with in a most effective manner. Instead of 'firefighter'-type management, whereby the project team jumps from one problem to another as they arise, project risk management enables a far calmer, more organised and proactive response to potential problems.

When probability analysis is utilised, the project management team also benefit from a more realistic forecast of a project's final cost or completion date, as both parameters will be shown in *ranges*, rather than single points. Traditional estimates for time and cost are lacking in that they often offer single values which imply certainty in a situation where such certainty cannot exist. Even where ranges are given using ± percentages, decision makers will still be unable to determine the *relative likelihood* of underruns or overruns. Probability analysis solves this problem and, therefore, improves decision makers' understanding which should, in turn, improve decisions.

Project risk management may be enhanced by VM by using the VM team to either audit or produce the project Risk Management Plan. In the former case, a prepared project Risk Management Plan may be submitted along with other information gathered for the VM study. This plan would be reviewed in detail during the Information phase and the VM team would determine whether, in their opinion, all the risk issues had been covered and that the assessment of those risk issues was reasonable. During the Creative phase the VM team may generate alternative ways to mitigate the various risk issues recognised. The remaining phases would be conducted in much the same way, except that proposals would be cognisant of risk issues and some proposals might be prepared purely to offer improved risk mitigation measures.

As a highly qualified multi-disciplinary team is already assembled, a VM study could also present the ideal opportunity for the initial formulation of the project Risk Management Plan. Under this approach, a *risk analysis specialist* would be added to the normal VM team. During the Information phase the additional activity of risk assessment will be undertaken after the team has a good understanding of the project from presentations and function analysis. The assessment may involve a 'negative brainstorming' session, whereby the team generates a list of the risk issues and then allocates qualitative measures to them. The team may also provide their forecasts of the quantitative consequences that these risks may have by assigning minimum, maximum and most likely values for time and cost estimate line items. Following this activity, the risk analyst would go away and process the information using a computerised simulation programme. The probabilistic risk analysis may then be introduced to the VM team prior to the Creative phase or merely be kept as a record of the risk profile of the original design. During the Creative phase, the VM team will generate measures which will mitigate the risk issues as well as generating the more usual type of ideas. The Evaluation phase would be conducted in the usual manner to sift out the best ideas. Towards the end of the Development phase, further quantitative risk analyses may be undertaken on specific proposals so that risk improvements relating to the proposals can be appreciated in a realistic manner.

Following the Implementation procedure, another project risk analysis may be prepared which will account for the actual proposals incorporated into the design. The risk assessment, analysis and mitigating measures derived from the VM study will be gathered to form the project Risk Management Plan which may thereafter be used in the normal manner.

Besides offering another productive use of the VM team, this approach may also present a relatively easy way of introducing project risk management into an organisation. Integration between VM and risk management can therefore be very advantageous.

VM and the Procurement Route

A plethora of procurement routes are used in construction today. These include conventional lump sum with a general contractor, design and build, management contracting, construction management and others, each of which have various advantages and disadvantages and differing risks and impacts with respect to time, cost and quality issues. For large scale projects the procurement strategy may become particularly complex, as the project may be too large for a single contract and may require the placement of a number of different contracts, some of which may have different procurement routes.

As the impact of the choice of procurement route is significant, a VM study should address this issue when appropriate. A Case Example of the type of proposal that may result with respect to procurement routes comes from a VM study on a large scale hospital project.

Case Example

During this study it was noted that the scale of the mechanical elements of space heating, air treatment, and ventilating systems was so large that only one subcontractor in the city in which the project was located would have the capacity to undertake the work. As this circumstance would, in effect, prevent competitive tendering, a VM proposal was put forward that these elements of work should be broken down. Breaking the scope of work down between several packages enabled competition, which could be expected to reduce costs, and the proposal was therefore accepted.

VM and Constructability Reviews

The ease with which a design can be constructed, i.e. its constructability or buildability can have a significant impact on costs. Under a traditional procurement route the project team involved during design may be expert in design issues, but less qualified when it comes to determining how their design will be built. This sometimes results in designs which impose severe limitations on contractors and thus causes their costs to grow unnecessarily. Often such constraints, if observed early enough, could be removed by modifying the design slightly to accommodate construction practices.

The inclusion of an expert on construction methods on the VM team enables the VM study to address any areas of the design which may cause undue cost due to a mismatch with construction practice. In addition, a construction expert may also address issues such as site operations, access and phasing, and similar aspects. These latter issues may be particularly important on refurbishment projects which require an organisation's operations to continue during construction, or where projects must be constructed on confined sites. Not only can proposals which improve constructability reduce costs, they can also save precious time from the programme.

Case Example

An example of this occurred during one VM study when the construction expert put forward a proposal pertaining to precast exterior wall panels.

Generally, designs for such systems offered only standard details for the connections between the panels and the superstructure, which meant that considerable time had to be spent on refining the designs while actually on site. By recommending that the design of precast wall panels be coordinated with that of the steel superstructure the construction expert caused significant reductions in the programme.

While under construction management and management contracting-type procurement routes the issues of constructability may be addressed during design phases, the incorporation of a constructability review with a VM study still makes sense. The combined effort, in effect, 'kills two birds with one stone'.

12 VM Professional Bodies and Training

12.1 VM Professional Bodies

There are a number of organisations around the world that have been established as professional VM societies to perpetuate VM in their respective countries. The original organisation, set up in VM's country of origin, is the Society of American Value Engineers (SAVE). This was established in 1958 and has since grown into a professional organisation with over a thousand members and is seen as the body which sets the standards for VM in the USA.

In the UK, the Institute of Value Management (IVM) is the primary professional body for VM. This Institute succeeded an early organisation called the Value Engineering Association, which was established in 1966.

We believe that the readers may potentially benefit from both organisations and, list their contact details in the Appendix on p. 221.

There are numerous other international VM organisations and contact details for them should be available from either IVM or SAVE.

12.2 VM Training

The proper training of the various individuals who will become involved with VM will obviously enhance its potential for success. Training can be considered under three categories according to the expected involvement of trainees. These categories are:

- Awareness training, for affected parties
- Participant training, for individuals who may act as team members
- Facilitator training, for those who will act as facilitators or VMTC

The different requirements for each of these training categories are now described.

Awareness Training

It is important for all parties affected by VM to be aware of the *process* and its *objectives*. In particular, it is highly advantageous to provide broad training for the senior and middle management of organisations which are introducing VM. Having gained awareness of the intentions of VM and how VM fits in with key organisational interests, management is more likely to be supportive of its implementation. Rather than merely being tolerant of yet another 'hoop to jump through', managers may become, through effective training, true VM champions.

The training content should reflect the needs of management and should, therefore, concentrate on the broader aspects of VM and its underlying philosophy rather than delving too deeply into the mechanics of the methodology. As management's time is usually a precious resource the training activities should also be of a short duration of perhaps a day or less. A typical one day awareness course agenda is shown in Working Document 12.1.

Participant Training

It is always better to use team members who have an understanding of both the broad *philosophy* of VM as well as the *mechanics* of the process. Effective training often appreciably increases team members' productivity and reduces interruptions that might otherwise be required to explain various VM techniques.

At the time of writing, there are no formally recognised guidelines for such training programmes in the UK. In the USA the SAVE has established guidelines for a formal training workshop (described as their Module I course) for individuals who may participate in VM studies under the guidance of qualified value specialists. While it should be recognised that cultural differences would probably necessitate modifications to the Module I workshop when used in the UK, it is considered that it provides a good basic framework for participant training and is therefore described below.

The Module I Workshop has a minimum duration of 40 hours and is tutored by a qualified value specialist. The course contents comprise both theoretical and practical 'hands on' instruction in equal proportions. In general, the theoretical portion of the course covers many of the issues covered in the parts I and II of this book. The practical portion involves taking trainees through a 'mock' VM study of a real project so that they may gain a better appreciation of the application of the theoretical techniques they are taught. The mock project is usually derived from an actual study previously undertaken by the value specialist.

The benefit of this approach is that trainees obtain an appreciation of the basic mechanics of VM prior to becoming involved with a VM study. This appreciation is not just theoretical but is deepened by applying the techniques to a 'mock' example. Armed with this understanding trainees may participate more effectively and efficiently in future studies.

Working Document 12.1   Typical one day awareness course agenda

TIME		AGENDA SUBJECT/TITLE
From	To	

9:00 AM	9:45 AM	**What VM Is, and What It Is Not**
		• Introduction
		• Background to VM
		• Future trends in VM
		• Definition of true VM
		  ○ Systematic
		  ○ Multi-disciplinary
		  ○ Function oriented
		  ○ Life cycle costing
		• Key terms and their meanings
		  ○ Value management
		  ○ Value planning, value engineering
		  ○ Value analysis
		• Professional bodies and their certification programmes
		  ○ British IVM
		  ○ SAVE
		  ○ Others

9:45	10:30	**When to Use VM** • Factors which contribute to poor value • Types of projects which benefit most from VM • How to select which projects upon which to use VM • Discussion
10:30	10:45	Break

10:45	12:45 PM	**How Authentic VM Is Performed**
		• Four basic approaches
		• Study timing
		• Study duration
		• Team structure
		• VM procedure
		  ➤ Pre-study phase
		  ➤ Study phase
		    ○ Job plans
		    ○ Information phase/Function Analysis
		    ○ Creative phase/Creativity Techniques
		    ○ Evaluation phase
		    ○ Development phase
		    ○ Presentation phase

		➤ Post-Study phase • Different study types, value planning and value engineering
12:45	1:30	Luncheon
1:30 PM	2:00 PM	**Organising the VM Programme** • Involving top management • Use of VM as a positive tool • VM coordinator activities • Selecting VM consultants/facilitators • VM facilitator activities • Implementation process • Dispute resolution process
2:00	2:30	**Linkages With Other Project Aspects** • VM and project management • VM and cost management • VM and risk management • VM and total quality management
2:30	3:00	**Why VM Is Effective**
3:00	4:00	**Client Project Management and VM Procedures**
4:00	5:00	**Conclusions and Discussion**

Facilitator Training

As may have been appreciated from earlier chapters, the facilitator's role in VM is not a straightforward one. His or her role entails both tangible elements such as guidance in the mechanics of the VM process, and intangible aspects involved with managing a dynamic team environment in a manner conducive to maximising results.

Education in the tangible aspects of the facilitator's role may be derived from more advanced theoretical seminars and further practice in the application of VM. Gaining an understanding of the intangible aspects is likely to be considerably more difficult. In SAVE's certification programme this difficulty may arguably be overcome by insisting on quite extensive experience of VM studies prior to qualification as a value specialist. Experience on its own, however, may not necessarily lead to understanding.

Appreciation of the intangible aspects of VM may perhaps best be attained by trainees by going through live VM studies in progressively responsible positions under the mentoring guidance of a qualified facilitator. Thus, the trainee may be involved as a team member on VM studies, initially, and then progress to the role of Assistant VMTC while the mentor acts as the VMTC/ lead facilitator. After an appropriate amount of experience these roles may be switched so that the trainee acts as VMTC/lead facilitator with the mentor's support as Assistant VMTC. Eventually the mentor's role may be dispersed with all together as the trainee becomes a fully proficient facilitator.

As each trainee will differ in the extent of their aptitude for VM, such an approach should be flexible and involve greater levels of training for those who need it. The extent of training required will be determined by the mentor, who will judge the level of competence gained by the trainee from 'feedback' discussions and from the results of the trainees' activities during the VM studies.

The importance of well trained facilitators should not be underestimated as the quality of a facilitator will have a direct and profound bearing on a VM study's results. It is important for a potential facilitator to gain a firm grounding in the basics of the *mechanics* of the process and then to progress to developing a capability in a facilitator's *less tangible* roles.

PART IV

Case Studies

13 Two VM Studies: An Infrastructure Project and a Hospital

13.1 Introduction

Chapter 13 considers case studies from two different project types: an infrastructure project and a hospital.

Case Study 1 was taken from a VP study of an infrastructure project. It describes, in considerable detail, the VM process conducted during the study and provides various completed pro formas that were included in the study report.

Case Study 2 comprises three sequential studies undertaken on the same hospital project. The first two were VP studies undertaken at the Briefing and Sketch Plans stages of the RIBA Plan of Work. The last was a VE study undertaken during the Detail Design stage.

Rather than repeat a detailed description of the VM process, which is essentially the same as for Case Study 1, Case Study 2 only provides a brief narrative which describes the main differences between each type of VM study. In addition, it provides samples of a number of documents that were produced during the study.

13.2 Case Study 1: VP Study of an Infrastructure Project

Project Description

The subject of this case study was a VP study of an infrastructure project. The study was conducted just prior to finalisation of the Brief. The Brief was well developed, with sketch plans indicating the layout of utilities and the like. A detailed *cost plan* had been developed, which indicated an estimated cost for the project of approximately £25 million.

The infrastructure project was one phase of a larger project which involved the consolidation of three large sites into one. This consolidation comprised the infrastructure project, several projects involving the construction of new buildings as well as the refurbishment of existing buildings. For the purposes of the subject VP study the location of the new buildings was fixed and thus the

187

infrastructure project had to serve both the new and existing buildings in their established positions. The infrastrucure work comprised the following elements:

- Boilers and cooling plant and distribution
- Natural gas
- Water supplies, potable, hydrant and softened
- Sprinkler system storage and distribution
- Foul and effluent drainage
- Electrical supply and distribution, voice and data, building management system and fire alarm networks
- Security, external works and miscellaneous minor buildings and builder's work.

A split study was chosen whereby the Information phase was conducted several days prior to the remaining phases of the study. This enabled time for the function analysis to be fully costed prior to the Creative phase of the job plan. Thus, the Information phase was conducted on the first day, and then the VP team disbanded while the function analysis was being costed. The VP team then reconvened to conduct the remaining phases of the job plan over a five day period. The study phase thus consisted of six days. The overall duration of the VP effort from Pre-study orientation to presentation of the final report was less than three weeks. The agenda for the study is shown in Working Document 13.1.

Working Document 13.1   Agenda for VP study of infrastructure project

DATE/ACTIVITY	TIME
Thursday, Week 1	
○ Introduction and discussion of VP objectives	9:00 AM
○ Design presentations (utilities, waste effluent, network systems, security, external works, buildings)	9:30 AM
○ Presentation by cost engineer	11:15 AM
○ Function analysis (by VP team only)	12:45 PM
○ Discussion of further information and allocation of gatherers	4:00 PM
○ Distribution of idea listing sheets and brief instruction in several creative techniques (individual and group)	4:20 PM
○ Final summation by VPTC	4:50 PM
Adjourn	5:00 PM
Friday, Week 1 – Wednesday, Week 2	
○ Develop function cost models outside study environment	

DATE/ACTIVITY	TIME

Thursday, Week 2

○ Writing up of ideas generated during break	8:45 AM
○ Introduction by VPTC	9:15 AM
○ Distribution and discussion of function analysis and cost models	9:30 AM
○ Verbal description of preliminary ideas by those that generated them	9:45 AM
○ Creative brainstorming session	11:00 AM
○ Evaluation of ideas	3:15 PM
○ Summation of VPTC	4:50 PM
Adjourn	5:00 PM

Friday, Week 2

○ Introduction by VPTC	8:45 AM
○ Review of ideas from overnight generation	9:00 AM
○ Evaluation of new ideas	9:45 AM
○ Reality check with user representatives/designers	10:15 AM
○ Allocate ideas for development	11:00 AM
○ Development of proposals	11:15 AM
○ Summation of VPTC	4:45 PM
○ Adjourn	5:00 PM
○ Introduction by VPTC	9:00 AM
○ Review of ideas from weekend gestation	9:15 AM
○ Evaluation of new ideas	10:00 AM
○ Allocate new ideas for development	10:30 AM
○ Development of proposals	11:00 AM
○ Final summation by VPTC	4:50 PM
Adjourn	5:00 PM

Tuesday, Week 3

○ Introduction by VPTC	8:45 AM
○ Development of proposals	9:00 AM
○ Discussion of presentation format and allocation of responsibilities	4:00 PM
○ Discussion of 'lessons learned'	4:30 PM
○ Final summation by VPTC	4:50 PM
Adjourn	5:00 PM

Wednesday, Week 3

○ Presentation of proposals to client management by core members of VP team (to be designated)	2:00 PM

Thursday and Friday, Week 3

○ Report preparation only by VPTC	

Team Structure

The VP team was made up of the following core members:

- Value Planning Team Coordinator (VPTC) (Associate Value Specialist)
- Assistant VPTC (Certified Value Specialist)
- Project manager
- Masterplan architect
- Mechanical engineer
- Electrical engineer
- Infrastructure/Civil engineer
- Estimator (supplemented during the development phase).

This team was supplemented by other interested parties who participated during the Information and/or Creative phases in particular. These other parties included the following:

- Senior client representatives
- Site operations representatives
- The security manager
- The communications manager
- The environmental manager
- The UK engineering manager.

The core VP team comprised a mix between members who had been involved with the project during design, together with several who had not. Part of the function of the latter group was to lend a degree of objectivity to the VM study.

Description of VP Study Activities

Pre-study Phase

During this phase, the logistics for the VP study were organised, and the VPTC and Assistant VPTC were given brief presentations on the project Master Plan and the mechanical and electrical content of the project.

Study Phase

Information phase   The objective of this phase was for the VP team to establish a good understanding of the project, its design and operation, the functions of the project itself, and its constituent elements, and to determine areas with the greatest potential for savings and needed improvements.

While the majority of team members had received prior presentations on the brief, or had contributed to it, some members had little prior knowledge of the project. With respect to those members who were already familiar with the project, their familiarity of the project was weighted toward their specific technical areas of expertise. In order to bring everyone's knowledge to a broadly comparable level and to uncover any misconceptions, presentations were given by the project manager and the mechanical and electrical engineers who had contributed to the Brief. These presentations were preceded by a brief address by the project director, who established the broad objectives of the VP study.

Following the design presentations, the VPTC and Assistant VPTC gave a brief overview of the VP process to be followed. Having completed the presentations a Function Analysis was undertaken by the team. The process of function analysis served two broad purposes:

1   To stimulate team discussion to uncover different members' *perceptions* of the functions of the project and its constituent elements
2   To highlight high cost functions which might be achieved equally well with a *less costly* design solution.

A function analysis was conducted on the overall project and then on each of the component elements of the project. Each function was described with a verb and noun, and was then rated as being Basic, Secondary or Required Secondary. The functions were then costed as shown in Working Document 13.2.

Following the Information phase meeting there was a four working day break in the VP process. During this interim period the functions listed during the information phase meeting were costed and graphic cost models were made of the elements of the cost plan, as shown in Figures 13.1 through 13.4.

Creative Phase

During the Creative phase, high cost areas were identified using a combination of the graphic elemental cost analyses and costed function analyses. Having established those elements with high costs, the team then underwent *group brainstorming* on each element respectively to generate 295 ideas.

No judgement was allowed during this phase so that team members would not be deterred from contributing ideas by criticism from others. In addition, team members were encouraged to think broadly which resulted in some wild, impractical ideas. While these wild ideas were not developed, they were valuable in that they served to prompt other ideas which could be usefully developed into proposals. Working Document 13.3 shows an excerpt from the idea listing.

Working Document 13.2 Information phase function analysis

INFORMATION PHASE FUNCTION ANALYSIS

PROJECT:		DATE:			PAGE: 1 of 2	
ITEM: Infrastructure		FUNCTION: Service Buildings				

ITEM NO.	DESCRIPTION	FUNCTION Verb	Noun	Kind	COST £	WORTH £	COMMENTS
05	Sprinklers	Manage	Risk	B	n/a		Higher order function
		Store	Water	S	130 000		Tanks
		Distribute	Water	B	180 000	100 000	Pipework
		Provide	Back-up	RS	84 000	84 000	Pumpset
		Screen	Vision	S	15 000		Around tanks
		House	Pumps	S	40 000		Building
	SUBTOTAL				**449 000**	**184 000**	**Value Index ≈ 2.44**
16	External works	Provide	Access	B	} 930 000		Roads
		Control	Access	B			
		Circulate	Vehicles	B			
		Access	Parking	B		850 000	
		Enhance	Convenience	S			
		Accommodate	Deliveries	B			
		Accommodate	Removals	B			
		Service	Buildings	B	250 000	150 000	Roads and retaining walls to loading bays
		Provide	Emergency Access	RS	} 225 000	200 000	Grasscrete areas
		Reduce	Congestion	RS		350 000	Section 52 works
		Satisfy	Regulations	RS			
	SUBTOTAL				**1755 000**	**1550 000**	

ACTION VERB
MEASURABLE NOUN

Kind { B = Basic / S = Secondary / RS = Required Secondary

(Basic Function Only)
Cost/Worth Ratio = _____

Working Document 13.2 (cont.)

INFORMATION PHASE FUNCTION ANALYSIS

PROJECT:			DATE:				
ITEM: Infrastructure			FUNCTION: Service Buildings				PAGE: 2 of 2
ITEM NO.	DESCRIPTION	FUNCTION			COST £	WORTH £	COMMENTS
		Verb	Noun	Kind			
16	External works (contd)	Separate	Vehicles	S	70 000		Visitor car parking
		Segregate	Parking	S			
		Enhance	Safety	RS			Lighting
		Illuminate	Roads	RS	200 000	200 000	
		Enhance	Security	S			
		Facilitate	Phase II	S	135 000		Site road replacement
		Satisfy	Planners	RS	140 000	140 000	Cycle way
		Store	Cars	B	700 000	700 000	Parking
		Store	Bicycles	S	70 000		Cycle shed
		Facilitate	Walking	B			Footpaths
		Direct	Walking	RS	310 000	275 000	
		Protect	Landscaping	S			
		Connect	Sites	S	450 000		
		Provide	Recreation	S	25 000		Benches, etc.
		Soften	Visual impact	RS	54 000	30 000	Landscaping to façade on Road X
		Enhance	Privacy	S	60 000		Landscaping buffer on south site
		Screen	Nuisances	RS			
		Enhance	Aesthetics	RS			
		Improve	Environment	B	2 100 000	1 500 000	Landscaping
		Elevate	Image	RS			
TOTAL					6 069 000	4 395 000	Value Index ≈ 1.4

ACTION VERB
MEASURABLE NOUN

Kind { B = Basic
S = Secondary
RS = Required Secondary

(Basic Function Only)
Cost/Worth Ratio =

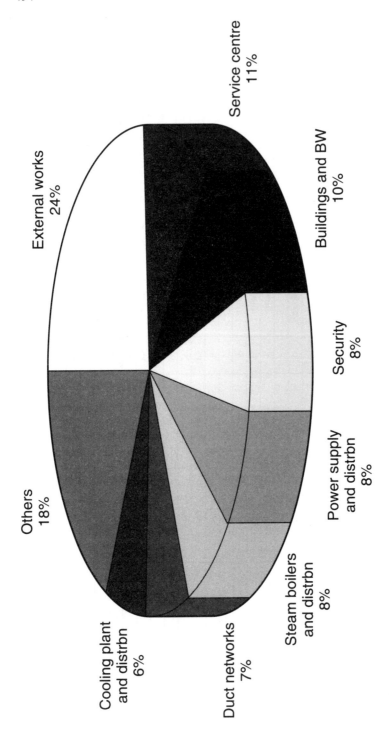

Figure 13.1   Pie Chart of Infrastructure Project Elements

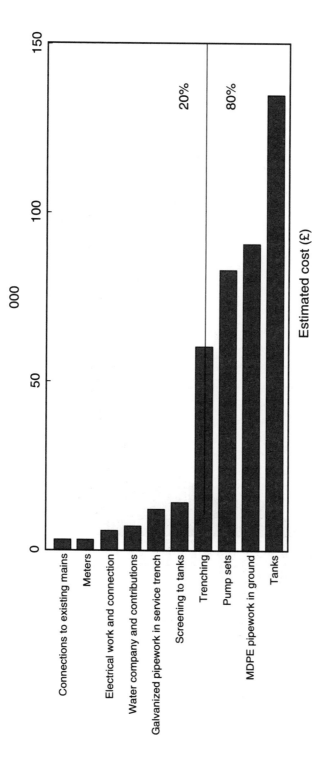

Figure 13.2   Elemental cost graph for sprinkler system

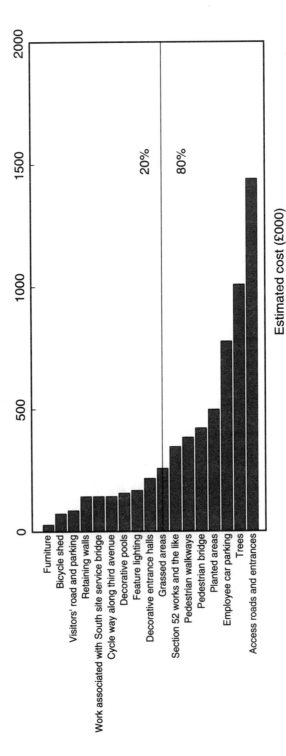

Figure 13.3   Elemental cost graph for external works

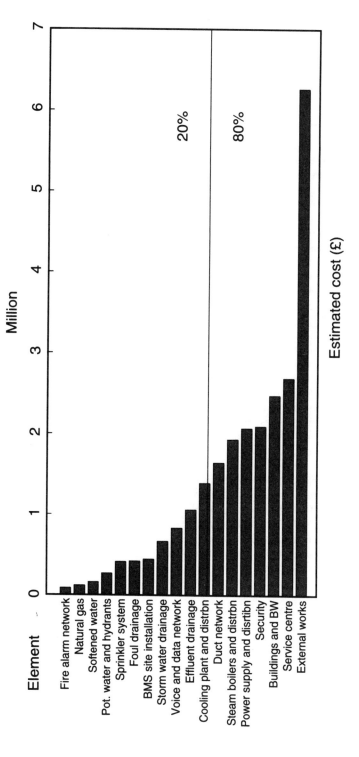

Figure 13.4   Elemental cost graph of infrastructure project

Working Document 13.3   Excerpt from ideas listing evaluation

	PROJECT: INFRASTRUCTURE VALUE PLANNING STUDY	PAGE: 1 of 1
ITEM	*DESCRIPTION*	*RATING*
SP-1	SPRINKLER SYSTEM	
SP-2	Deleted	
SP-3	Reduce sprinkler areas	2
SP-4	Reduce distance between sprinkler heads	4
SP-5	Pond storage in lieu of tanks	4
SP-6	Direct mains feed system in lieu of tanks?	1
SP-7	Position tanks in buildings	4
SP-8	Localise tanks – additional tanks/pumps to north	4
SP-9	Combine sprinkler and bulk water storage tanks	4
SP-10	Diesel engine in lieu of standby generator	2
SP-11	Remove tank screening	3
SP-12	Storage tanks placed in Ha Ha	4
	Use SW to reinforce sprinkler requirement	4
EX-1	EXTERNAL WORKS	
EX-2	Eliminate access road upgrade	4
EX-3	Close access road	4
EX-41	Retain existing road on South site (serving Phase II)	1
EX-42	Gas in lieu of electric street lights	DS*
EX-43	One way road system in lieu of two way	1
	Narrow new estate roads and add passing places in lieu of	1
EX-44	wide two way roads	
EX-45	Eliminate cycle shed and add alternative	1
EX-46	Basement cycle storage in lieu of bike shed	4
EX-47	Eliminate covered walkways	1
EX-72	Increase street lighting levels	3
EX-73	Artificial gas in lieu of real	4
EX-74	Use sheep for grass cutting	4
EX-75	Eliminate decorative pools	1
EX-76	Reduce entrance decoration by 50%	1
	Subsidise public transport	4

*DS = Design Suggestion

Evaluation Phase

During this phase, the ideas generated during the Creative phase were evaluated to sift out impractical ideas and to identify the best ideas for development.

The rating technique used for evaluation purposes was as follows:

Rating   Idea treatment
1   Ideas to be developed
2   Ideas to be developed if sufficient time is available
3   Ideas with some merit but was not considered to be worth developing
4   Ideas havelittle merit and not to be developed.

Working Document 13.4 summarises the number of ideas remaining after judgement. Thus, out of 295 initial ideas, some 74 were rated with a score of 1 or noted as a design suggestion. Another 30 were rated with a score of 2 and would thus be developed only if sufficient time was available.

Development Phase

During this phase the ideas selected during the preceding evaluation phase were refined and developed into *proposals*.

Working Document 13.4   Summary of ideas and judgement rating

ELEMENT	TOTAL OF IDEAS	VP RATING SCORE*		DESIGN SUGGESTION
		1	2	
Steam boilers and distribution	33	1	1	8
Cooling plant and distribution	16	0	0	0
Natural gas	1	0	1	0
Water supplies	4	0	2	0
Sprinkler system	12	1	2	0
Effluent drainage	11	1	0	0
Foul drainage	3	0	1	0
Storm water drainage	9	0	3	0
Duct networks	6	3	0	0
HV supplies/power distribution	21	2	2	2
Voice and data networks	12	3	0	0
BMS site installation	12	5	1	0
Security	31	8	3	0
Fire alarm network	5	3	0	0
Service centre	20	7	1	0
External works	79	19	12	3
Buildings and builders work	20	8	1	1
TOTALS	**295**	**60**	**30**	**14**

1.   Ideas to be developed.
2.   Ideas to be developed if sufficient time is available.

Detailed calculations were developed, and each proposal included:

- Descriptions of original and proposed revised design
- Discussion of advantages and disadvantages of proposal
- Initial and life cycle (LCC) cost savings (where appropriate)
- Technical calculations, sketches and other backup.

Examples of proposal cover sheets are shown in Working Documents 13.5 and 13.6. Typical summaries of proposals are shown in Working Document 13.7.

Working Document 13.5   VP proposal: 1

PROJECT: CASE STUDY		DATE:	
PROPOSAL: Direct mains feed to sprinkler systems in lieu of storage tanks		*NO:* SP-5	
		PAGE: 1 of 1	

ORIGINAL DESIGN:
Sprinkler systems are fed by a 150 m^3 storage tank and pumps. Sprinkler system to Building C is fed by a 450 m^3 storage tank on South site. All tanks are fed from incoming mains.
PROPOSED CHANGE:
Feed sprinklers directly from mains on both sites and eliminate storage tanks and pumps.
ADVANTAGES:
Cost reduction by the elimination of tanks and pumps.
Reduced maintenance due to elimination of pumps.
DISADVANTAGES:
Risk of sprinkler failure due to incoming mains failure/pressure reduction – original design is independent of mains once tanks are full.
DISCUSSION:
Check required with insurance company on their requirements together with discussion with risk management before this proposal is carried any further.

LIFE CYCLE COST SUMMARY	*INITIAL COST*	*O and M COST*		*TOTAL LIFE CYCLE COST £*
		Each year	*Life cycle*	
Original design	400 000			400 000
VP proposal	200 000			200 000
Savings	200 000			200 000

Working Document 13.6   VP Proposal 2

PROJECT: CASE STUDY	DATE:	
PROPOSAL: Locate site effluent tanks above ground		NO: ED-3
		PAGE: 1 of 1

ORIGINAL DESIGN:
Currently effluent holding tanks area located below ground in fully accessible chambers. Therefore, they are seen from offices or access roads.
PROPOSED CHANGE:
Locate holding tanks above ground to the south of Building D where they cannot be seen from offices or access road. An additional pumping station may be required due to the topography along the route of the effluent main.
ADVANTAGES:
Reduction in cost due to elimination of underground chamber.
DISADVANTAGES:
The tanks and pumps will be seen from the neighbouring housing estate and will therefore need to be screened.
An additional pumping set.
DISCUSSION:
The cost reduction of the underground chamber will more than offset the increased cost of screening and additional pumping set as seen from the estimate.

LIFE CYCLE COST SUMMARY	INITIAL COST	O & M COST		TOTAL LIFE CYCLE COST £
		Each year	Life cycle	
Original design	1 050 000			1 050 000
VP proposal	900 000			900 000
Savings	150 000			150 000

Presentation Phase

A meeting was convened at the end of the VP study to present the major proposals to management representatives and to obtain their preliminary decisions regarding proposal selections.

Conclusions

The outcome of the study was a success in that approximately £3 million net, or approximately 12% of the original estimated cost, had been saved without reducing the required project functions. This net total included several project improvement proposals which added cost of approximately

Working Document 13.7   Summary of VP proposals

PROJECT: CASE STUDY   DATE: PAGE: 1 of 1

ITEM NO.	DESCRIPTION	ORIGINAL DESIGN COST	VP PROPOSAL COST	PRESENT WORTH OF COST SAVINGS		
				Initial cost savings	LCC O and M cost savings	Total LCC cost savings
		£	£	£	£	£
SPRINKLER SYSTEM						
SP-5	Direct mains feed to sprinkler system in lieu of storage tank	400 000	200 000	200 000		200 000
HV SUPPLIES/POWER DISTRIBUTION						
E-1	Direct bury HV and LV distribution in lieu of ducts	600 000	350 000	250 000		250 000
E-3	Eliminate North–South cable links and retain board supplies	1 850 000	1 750 000	100 000	TBD	100 000
E-13	Eliminate 33KV substation, accept 11KV supplies only					DS
E-14	Reduce power requirements by using variable volume fume cupboards					DS
EXTERNAL WORKS						
EX-3	Retain existing road on South site to front and side of Building A	10 000	10 000			140 000
EX-8	Delete separate entrance to visitor's parking on Road (N)	10 000				10 000
EX-9	Eliminate widening of Road A and stack cars within site	100 000	50 000			50 000
EX-11	Retain east site parking and locate building elsewhere	400 000				400 000
EX-13	Enter from existing site entrance and eliminate new entrance	120 000	20 000			100 000
EX-22	Reduce height of retaining walls to loading bay	105 000	50 000			55 000
EX-23	Relocate basement loading dock		(75 000)			DS
EX-31	Provide dedicated delivery bay to basement of Building B	160 000	30 000			(75 000)
EX-39	Provide external building floodlights in lieu of street lighting					30 000
EX-40	Increase spacing between external lighting columns/bollards					DS
EX-42	Provide one way road system in lieu of two way	135 000	40 000			40 000
EX-43	Narrow new estate roads to 5m	100 000	100 000			100 000
EX-44	Reduce provision and specification for bike storage	70 000	50 000			50 000
EX-46	Eliminate covered walkways	90 000	90 000			90 000
EX-49	Provide space for service vehicle parking					DS
EX-64	Eliminate planted screening to boundaries	20 000	20 000			20 000
EX-74	Eliminate decorative pools and replace with planted beds	150 000	75 000			75 000

£100 000. Proposals amounting to £1 170 000 were deferred during the implementation meeting. Costs in use of LCC savings were not calculated, owing to a lack of required data at the time of the study.

When considering the deferred proposals, the results of the study ranged between initial cost savings of 12–16%, which was reasonable for a VP study.

13.3 Case Study 2: VP and VE Studies of a Hospital Project

Project Description

This project provided for the renovation of 40,000 square metres in an existing, publicly owned hospital and the construction of 20,000 square metres of new space. The total size of the facility, including unrenovated space, was 95,000 square metres. The total budget for the project was £130 million for all costs, including professional service fees, construction, equipment, etc.

This amount was fixed, and it was clear that no additional funding would be forthcoming. The VM effort was initiated in order to get maximum benefit from the limited funding and to assure that project costs would be strictly contained as the design process advanced. Due to the project's size and complexity three VM studies were programmed – Study 1 at the Brief Stage, Study 2 at the Sketch plans stage and Study 3 at the Detail Design stage.

Studies 1 and 2 were VP studies and Study 3 was a VE study. By programming the studies at these project milestone points major redesign, resulting from VM, was avoided since the VM proposals implemented could be incorporated in the following design phase without having to change work that had already been completed.

Description of VP and VE Activities

Study 1: Brief Stage

The overall direction of this VP study was to examine 'what' was to be constructed rather than 'how' it was to be constructed. In addition, the study differed significantly from a typical VM study wherein each phase of the study – Information, Creative, Evaluation and Development – is completed for the entire project before moving on to the next study phase. This study could not follow that procedure because the bulk of this workshop was devoted to a space by space review of the function and space programmes, thus requiring completion of the review for each space before moving on to the next. In effect, mini-VM studies were conducted for each and every space under review, and each of the VM study phases was repeated over and over for each space. The time devoted to each space was minimised, and in many cases lasted for only minutes. Because of the great number of spaces and the time limitations this work was divided among three subteams. The agenda for the study is shown in Working Document 13.8.

Working Document 13.8   Agenda for functional programme review of a hospital

---

DAY ONE

8:30 AM	INTRODUCTION
8:35	OBJECTIVES OF REVIEW
8:45	PROJECT STATUS

Overall status – Owner representatives
Project constraints

9:00   STATUS OF DESIGN
Proposed programme areas
Owner and designer
Concept, criteria, budget, and proposed operational mode

10:00   TEAM REVIEW OF LATEST PROGRAMME DOCUMENTS AND ESTIMATES
Study latest documents
Update and review project cost model, LCC model, space models
Analyse methods
Select high cost elements
Divide into subteams

12:30 PM   LUNCH

1:30   IDEA PHASE: CYCLE No. 1 (SUBTEAMS)
Individual: Identify space functions of program organisational categories
Propose alternatives and establish space/staffing targets

3:30   Group: Discuss proposed alternatives and space/staffing targets

5:00   ADJOURN

DAY TWO

8:30 AM   IDEA PHASE: CYCLE No. 2 (FULL TEAM)
Group: Discuss proposed alternative and space/staffing targets
Individual: Identify functions of major cost elements, proposed revised alternatives and space/staffing targets

12:30 PM   LUNCH

1:30   GROUP CONSENSUS (SUB-TEAMS)
Summarise key ideas from cycle No. 2
Estimate savings potential
Identify most promising ideas for discussion

3:00   IDEA PHASE REVIEW (FULL TEAM)
Present most promising ideas by each subteam and summarize savings potential

5:00   ADJOURN

DAY THREE

8:30 AM   EVALUATION PHASE ORGANISATION (FULL TEAM)
Prioritise ideas by saving potential, need for input from several team members, etc.
Subteam assignment of priority element
Discuss remaining tasks to be completed

12:30 PM   LUNCH

1:30   EVALUATION PHASE (SUBTEAMS)
Individual assignment of ideas for development
Sketches, estimates, calculations
Weighted evaluation
LCC analysis

5:00   ADJOURN

DAY FOUR

8:30 AM   REVIEW STATUS & PROGRESS
Ideas developed and savings identified
Ideas yet to be developed
Tasks remaining

10:30   DEVELOPMENT PHASE
Sketches, cost estimates, calculations
Weighted evaluation
LCC analysis

12:30 PM   LUNCH

1:30   DEVELOPMENT PHASE (SUBTEAMS)
Summary of changes (original, proposed, discussion)
Summary of costs and savings

5:00   ADJOURN

DAY FIVE

8:30 AM   PRESENTATION PHASE
Presentation of Recommendations

- Initial cost savings
- Staffing/operational cost savings
- Schedule

Tasks still remaining and people responsible
Follow up responsibilities
Summary of results of functional programme review

11:30   CLOSING REMARKS
Project manager – client
Designer
Value engineer

12:30 PM   ADJOURN

The VP proposals, which deal with space rather than costs, were separated into six groups:
(A) Nursing, (B) Professional Services, (C) Mental Hygiene, (D) Ambulatory Care, (E) Support Services and (F) Administration. Working Document 13.9 shows a summary of these groups, Group (A) Nursing, and Working Document 13.10 shows one of the individual proposals from this group.

The agendas for study 2 and study 3 followed a typical agenda for 40 hour VM studies. The bulk of the first day was devoted to the Information phase, starting with a project presentation by the client and the design team, with a question and answer period. This was followed by a period during which the individual VM team members were given the opportunity to become familiar with the available project documents, and this was followed by function analysis. The second day was primarily devoted to the Creative phase, and on the morning of the third day the Evaluation phase was completed. The Development phase started in the afternoon of the third day and continued through the fourth day and the morning of the fifth day. The VM teams' proposals were presented to the client and the design team during the Presentation phase which occurred in the afternoon of the fifth and last day of the workshops. One of these agendas, that for Study 3, is shown in Working Document 13.11.

Study 2

Because this study was undertaken at a very early stage of design development, it was possible to consider significant *design modifications*, since they would have minimal impact on the work already completed. Again the emphasis was on 'what' not 'how'. Therefore, the VM effort focused on more global design considerations. Working Document 13.12 is one page from the 'Summary of Cost savings' showing part of the list of architectural proposals, and Working Document 13.13 shows one of the listed proposals.

Study 3

This study was a typical design orientated VE study. It focused on 'how' the project was to be constructed. Function Analysis on each design discipline was performed during the Information phase, and this was followed by idea generation during the Creative phase. Ideas which survived the Evaluation phase were then fleshed out and written-up during Development phase. Working Documents 13.14, 13.15 and 13.16 show the progression through the VM process for one element, the intercom system, in the electrical part of the design.

Working Document 13.9   Summary of space reductions from VE recommendations

PROJECT: HOSPITAL			DATE:		PAGE: 4 of 14	
ITEM NO.	DESCRIPTION	ORIGINAL DESIGN M²	VP PROPOSAL M²	PRESENT WORTH OF COST SAVINGS		
				Initial space reduction M²		Total space reduction
	NURSING					
A-1	Increase capacity of medical/surgical nursing units for 39 beds	7 575	7 424	133	NA	133
A–2	Reduce size of nursing unit support facilities	2 301	463	1 838	NA	1 838
A–4	Change patient room mix	2 304	1 935	99	NA	99
A–5	Revise programme for operating suite/ambulatory surgery	3 228	3 058	170	NA	170
A–11	Revise labour and delivery programme	1 124	1 054	70	NA	70
	NA – Not Applicable					

Working Document 13.10   Value planning proposal

PROJECT: HOSPITAL	DATE:
PROPOSAL: Reduce area of nursing unit support space	NO: A-2
	PAGE: 1 of 4

ORIGINAL DESIGN:
A separate programme provides six support units. One per floor for nursing except SNF. The support unit presumes the cluster design for nursing units. There is some duplication of functions in the nursing unit and support unit.
PROPOSED CHANGE:
The VP team recommends a significant reduction in the size of the support unit by eliminating the duplication of functions. The spaces that have been eliminated resulted in some increase in the size of the corresponding element in the nursing unit. This proposal then is linked with A–1. This suggests a non-cluster double corridor design with most support in the patient care unit.
ADVANTAGES:
DISADVANTAGES:
DISCUSSION:
Floor support unit retains visitor/patient lounge, classroom and on call on resident facilities.
Centralising support services on each unit increases operational efficiency as well as reducing square metre requirements.
Concerns: Need for diagram of proposed double corridor to determine feasibility.

SPACE SUMMARY	INITIAL SPACE	O AND M COST		TOTAL SPACE M^2
		Each Year	Life Cycle	
Original Design	2 301			2 301
VP Proposal	463			463
Savings	1 838			1 838

Working Document 13.11   Agenda for VP Study of Hospital Project

MONDAY

9:30 AM   TEAM MEMBERS ARRIVE

10:30   INTRODUCTION TO WORKSHOP
Objectives of workshop
Workshop format
Team members

12:00 PM   LUNCH

1:00   CONTINUATION OF DISCUSSIONS WITH DESIGNERS (if required)

DESIGNER/CLIENT
Overview
Constraints
Open issues
Major systems
Question and answers

TEAM REVIEW OF DESIGN DOCUMENTS & COST MODELS
Study latest drawings and specifications
Review cost, energy, and LCC models

4:00   FUNCTION ANALYSIS
Use of cost, energy, and LCC models to target worth
Graphical analysis and FAST diagram (as appropriate)
Selection of high cost elements
Start function analysis

6:00   ADJOURN

THURSDAY

8:00 AM   DEVELOPMENT PHASE
Prepare design alternatives
Prepare LCC analysis
Estimates, calculations and sketches

12:00 PM   LUNCH

1:00   DEVELOPMENT PHASE (Contd)
Criteria weighting
Matrix evaluation of alternatives
Costing of alternatives
LCC analysis

3:00   DEVELOPMENT PHASE/RECOMMENDATIONS
Written recommendations

6:00   ADJOURN

FRIDAY

8:00 AM   COMPLETE PROPOSALS
Completion of written proposals/report
Prepare summary of recommendations and savings potential
Complete presentation materials
Prepare draft VE report

12:00 PM   LUNCH

1:00   PRESENTATION OF RECOMMENDATIONS

3:00   ADJOURN

Working Document 13.12   Summary of potential cost savings from VE recommendations

PROJECT: CITY HOSPITAL			DATE:		PAGE:1 of 1		
		ORIGINAL DESIGN COST	VP PROPOSAL COST	PRESENT WORTH OF COST SAVINGS			
ITEM NO.	DESCRIPTION			Initial Cost Savings	LCC O and M Cost Savings	Total LCC Cost Savings	
		£	£	£	£	£	
	ARCHITECTURAL						
A–1	Simplify design of West end of ambulatory care facility			190 000		190 000	
A–2	Eliminate outdoor terrace level 2			40 000		40 000	
A–5	Eliminate unneeded mechanical and equipment space over East end ambulatory care facility			300 000		300 000	
A–6	Eliminate interior lightwells, ambulatory care facility			450 000		450 000	
A–7	Reduce area of ambulatory care lobby			324 000		324 000	
A–10	Eliminate waiting area extension over ambulatory care facility			15 000		15 000	
A–11	entrance						
	Change circular stair to rectangular in ambulatory care facility lobby			60 000		60 000	
A–12	Revise stairs at end of A and B wing additions			20 000		20 000	
A–14	Eliminate provision for future vertical expansion of ambulatory care facility			125 000		125 000	
A–17	Use masonry for exterior walls			1 359 000		1 359 000	
A–19	Eliminate C wing stairs and use existing stairs			94 000		94 000	
A–21	Use 2 plys of gypsum board on studs in lieu of concrete brick partitions in corridors			454 000		454 000	

Working Document 13.13 *VP proposal*

PROJECT: HOSPITAL	DATE:
PROPOSAL: Reduce area of ambulatory care facility lobby	NO: A–17
	PAGE: 1 of 4

ORIGINAL DESIGN:
Existing concept has entrance lobby of 45 x 18 ± with 3m corridors on each side of core functions.
PROPOSED CHANGE:
VE concept reduces by 3m utilising one 5m corridor adjacent to the core functions. Reduction is 135m^2 x 3 floors = 405m^2 plus reductions in penthouse roof and exterior wall area.
ADVANTAGES:
DISADVANTAGES:
DISCUSSION:

LIFE CYCLE COST SUMMARY	INITIAL COST	O & M COST		TOTAL LIFE CYCLE COST £
		Each year	Life cycle	
Original design				
VP proposal				
Savings	324 000			324 000

Team Structure

Appropriate team members were selected for each study 1–3, based on the stage of the design and the types of documents which would be available at that point in the design development process.

For Study 1, at the Project Brief stage, the main documents to be reviewed were the functional programme and the space allocation programmes. Accordingly, the VM team structure emphasised space planning and materials handling experts. Three space planning experts were used to permit a comprehensive review of all of the various project's elements during the time frame of the study. Materials handling experts were also included on the VM team to evaluate the various systems because movement of patients, staff and materials is a particularly critical aspect in hospital design.

For Study 2, at the Sketch Plans stage, the team included both planning experts and technical design experts from various disciplines. This was done because the documents under review reflected the translation of the functional and space programmes to the hospital's layout and design, including: architectural, structural, mechanical, electrical and materials handling.

Working Document 13.14 Function analysis worksheet[1]

INFORMATION PHASE FUNCTION ANALYSIS

PROJECT: Hospital

DATE:

PAGE: 1 of 2

ITEM: Electrical

FUNCTION Service buildings

ITEM NO.	DESCRIPTION	Verb	Noun	Kind	COST £	WORTH £	COMMENTS
	TV system	Entertain	Patients	S	109 000	100 000	Review scope
	Data communications	Access	Information	B	35 000	33 000	
	Security System	Improve	Safety	S	277 000	200 000	
	Mechanical–HVAC system	Energise	Systems	B	37 000	37 000	
	Demolition	Prepare	Site	S	90 000	90 000	
	Nurses call system	Enable	Communication	B	615 000	437 000	Reduce scope
	Intercom	Enable	Communication	S	56 000	11 000	Reduce scope
	(Fire Alarm)	Improve	Safety	B	213 000	200 000	

ACTION VERB

MEASURABLE NOUN

Kind { B = Basic / S = Secondary / RS = Required Secondary

(Basic Function Only) _____

Cost/Worth Ratio = _____

Working Document 13.15   Creative idea listing

PROJECT:	CITY HOSPITAL – CREATIVE/EVALUATION WORKSHEET	PAGE: 1 of 1
ITEM	DESCRIPTION	RATING
E–1	Provide padlocks at starters in motor control centre and delete disconnects at motors in same room with motor control centre	8
E–2	Provide spaces for future mechanical loads	7
E–5	Revise/change feeder sizes	10
E–10	Reduce lighting level in corridors	10
E–14	Locate automatic transfer switch No. 4 in basement near switch No. 3	10
E–15	Delete automatic transfer switch No. 4 and feeder DS-2CHs and feed directly from DS-2BEM	10
E–17	Revise cost estimate for nurse call to share signal cable tray with other systems	10
E–18	Revise security system cost estimate to utilise signal tray for runs in corridors	10
E–20	Use telephone for all intercom – delete the dedicated system.	9
E–21	Show load analysis, lighting load, receptacles, and motor loads	6
E–22	Incorporate part of new switchboard room into mechanical spaces	10
E–23	Consider use of one 900KW generator in lieu of 3-450KW?	6

˙ DS = Design suggestion

For Study 3, at the Detail Design stage (about the 35% design completion point), the team was structured to emphasise primarily a review of the various design disciplines. Planning experts, who were involved in the earlier VM studies, were also included on the VM team to provide support and background to the technical design team members.

Because of the complexity of the project an Assistant Value Management team coordinator (AVMTC) was included for each of studies. An estimator/QS was also included to assure the accuracy of the cost estimating relative to all of the proposals developed by the VM team and, for each study, the client's VM project manager was also present.

Representatives from a number of public agencies also attended each of the studies, along with administration personnel from the hospital. However, it should be noted that their participation was limited to providing additional information, as needed, to the external VM team members. Their participation was limited because the client agency, an oversight public agency, wanted the

Working Document 13.16   Summary of potential cost savings from VE recommendations

PROJECT: CITY HOSPITAL			DATE:		PAGE: 1 of 1	
				PRESENT WORTH OF COST SAVINGS		
ITEM NO.	DESCRIPTION	ORIGINAL DESIGN COST	VP PROPOSAL COST	Initial cost savings	LCC O and M cost savings	Total LCC cost savings
		£	£	£	£	£
E-1	Provide padlocks at starters in motor control centre and delete disconnects at motors in same room with motor control centre			12 900		12 900
E-2	Provide space for future mechanical loads			5 500		5 500
E-5	Revise/change feeder sizes			5 300		5 300
E-10	Reduce lighting level in corridors			230 200		230 200
E-14	Locate automatic transfer switch No. 4 in basement near switch No. 3			4 300		4 300
E-15	Delete automatic transfer switch No. 4 and feeder DS-2CHS and feed directly from DS-2BEM			8 700		8 700
E-17	Revise cost estimate for nurse call system to share signal cable tray with other system			311 000		311 000
E-18	Revise security system cost estimate to utilise signal tray			See E-17		See E-17
E-20	Delete intercom system, use telephone			37 000		37 000
E-22	Incorporate part of new switch board room into mechanical spaces			173 000		173 000

Working Document 13.17   Team structures for multiple VM studies of a hospital

VP Study # 1 (Project Brief)	VP Study # 2 (Sketch Plans)	VE Study # 3 (Detail Design)
Core Team VMTC Assistant VMTC Three (3) Space Planning Experts Two (2) Materials Handling Experts Estimator	*Core Team* VMTC Assistant VMTC Architect Structural Engineer Electrical Engineer Heating and Ventilating Engineer Plumbing Engineer Two (2) Hospital Experts Materials Handling Expert Estimator	*Core Team* VMTC Assistant VMTC Architect Structural Engineer Electrical Engineer Mechanical Engineer Two (2) Hospital Experts Materials Handling Expert Estimator
Client Representatives Mayor's Office – Construction representative Mayor's Office - Administration Representative Two (2) Hospital Administrators Two (2) Project Managers Budget Agency Representative Value Management Project Manager	*Client Representatives* Hospital Project Manager Central Office Architect Central Office Electrical Engineer Value Management Project Manager	*Client Representatives* Hospital Project Manager Central Office Architect Central Office Mechanical Engineer

VM studies to be seen as fully independent, outside, second, expert opinions. Working Document 13.17 shows the team structure for each of the three studies.

Conclusion

Prior to each of the VM studies 1–3, cost estimates were prepared which showed that the project's costs were exceeding the budget allowance. At the Brief stage the estimate showed that all of the work contemplated could not be completed within the budget allowance. At the Sketch plans and the Detail Design stages it was evident that 'scope creep' was occurring with concurrent cost growth. However, sufficient cost reducing VM proposals were accepted by all of the interested parties at the conclusion of each study to get the project back on track. For study 1, the amount of savings was £15.8 million, for Study 2, the amount was £19.1 million, and for the Study 3, the amount was £.43 million. These results clearly demonstrate the success of this VM effort. However, an even more meaningful result followed from this VM project.

This project was one of the first selected by this public agency to test the effectiveness of VM as part of an overall cost management programme. Partly because the results achieved on this project were so positive, this agency decided to apply VM to all major projects in its £2.0 billion/year capital programme. Over time, that initiative was fully implemented and this public agency's VM programme, which encompasses a very wide variety of project types, is widely regarded as a model.

Appendix 1

Appendix 1 (A)
Present Value of £1 Table

Year	5%	6%	7%	8%	9%	10%	11%	12%	13%	14%	15%
1	0.952381	0.943396	0.934579	0.925926	0.917431	0.909091	0.900901	0.892857	0.884956	0.877193	0.869565
2	0.907029	0.889996	0.873439	0.857339	0.841680	0.826446	0.811622	0.797194	0.783147	0.769468	0.756144
3	0.863838	0.839619	0.816298	0.793832	0.772183	0.751315	0.731191	0.711780	0.693050	0.674972	0.657516
4	0.822702	0.792094	0.762895	0.735030	0.708425	0.683013	0.658731	0.635518	0.613319	0.592080	0.571753
5	0.783526	0.747258	0.712986	0.680583	0.649931	0.620921	0.593451	0.567427	0.542760	0.519369	0.497177
6	0.746215	0.704961	0.666342	0.630170	0.596267	0.564474	0.534641	0.506631	0.480319	0.455587	0.432328
7	0.710681	0.665057	0.622750	0.583490	0.547034	0.513158	0.481658	0.452349	0.425061	0.399637	0.375937
8	0.676839	0.627412	0.582009	0.540269	0.501866	0.466507	0.433926	0.403883	0.376160	0.350559	0.326902
9	0.644609	0.591898	0.543934	0.500249	0.460428	0.424098	0.390925	0.360610	0.332885	0.307508	0.284262
10	0.613913	0.558395	0.508349	0.463193	0.422411	0.385543	0.352184	0.321973	0.294588	0.269744	0.247185
11	0.584679	0.526788	0.475093	0.428883	0.387533	0.350494	0.317283	0.287476	0.260698	0.236617	0.214943
12	0.556837	0.496969	0.444012	0.397114	0.355535	0.318631	0.285841	0.256675	0.230706	0.207559	0.186907
13	0.530321	0.468839	0.414964	0.367698	0.326179	0.289664	0.257514	0.229174	0.204165	0.182069	0.162528
14	0.505068	0.442301	0.387817	0.340461	0.299246	0.263331	0.231995	0.204620	0.180677	0.159710	0.141329
15	0.481017	0.417265	0.362446	0.315242	0.274538	0.239392	0.209004	0.182696	0.159891	0.140096	0.122894
16	0.458112	0.393646	0.338735	0.291890	0.251870	0.217629	0.188292	0.163122	0.141496	0.122892	0.106865
17	0.436297	0.371364	0.316574	0.270269	0.231073	0.197845	0.169633	0.145644	0.125218	0.107800	0.092926
18	0.415521	0.350344	0.295864	0.250249	0.211994	0.179859	0.152822	0.130040	0.110812	0.094561	0.080805
19	0.395734	0.330513	0.276508	0.231712	0.194490	0.163508	0.137678	0.116107	0.098064	0.082948	0.070265
20	0.376889	0.311805	0.258419	0.214548	0.178431	0.148644	0.124034	0.103667	0.086782	0.072762	0.061100
21	0.358942	0.294155	0.241513	0.198656	0.163698	0.135131	0.111742	0.092560	0.076798	0.063826	0.053131
22	0.341850	0.277505	0.225713	0.183941	0.150182	0.122846	0.100669	0.082643	0.067963	0.055988	0.046201
23	0.325571	0.261797	0.210947	0.170315	0.137781	0.111678	0.090693	0.073788	0.060144	0.049112	0.040174
24	0.310068	0.246979	0.197147	0.157699	0.126405	0.101526	0.081705	0.065882	0.053225	0.043081	0.034934
25	0.295303	0.232999	0.184249	0.146018	0.115968	0.092296	0.073608	0.058823	0.047102	0.037790	0.030378

Appendix 1 (B)
Present Value of £1 per Annum Table

Year	5%	6%	7%	8%	9%	10%	11%	12%	13%	14%	15%
1	1.0000	1.0000	1.0000	1.0000	1.0000	1.0000	1.0000	1.0000	1.0000	1.0000	1.0000
2	2.0500	2.0600	2.0700	2.0800	2.0900	2.1000	2.1100	2.1200	2.1300	2.1400	2.1500
3	3.1525	3.1836	3.2149	3.2464	3.2781	3.3100	3.3421	3.3744	3.4069	3.4396	3.4725
4	4.3101	4.3746	4.4399	4.5061	4.5731	4.6410	4.7097	4.7793	4.8498	4.9211	4.9934
5	5.5256	5.6371	5.7507	5.8666	5.9847	6.1051	6.2278	6.3528	6.4803	6.6101	6.7424
6	6.8019	6.9753	7.1533	7.3359	7.5233	7.7156	7.9129	8.1152	8.3227	8.5355	8.7537
7	8.1420	8.3938	8.6540	8.9228	9.2004	9.4872	9.7833	10.0890	10.4047	10.7305	11.0668
8	9.5491	9.8976	10.2598	10.6366	11.0285	11.4359	11.8594	12.2997	12.7573	13.2328	13.7268
9	11.0266	11.4913	11.9780	12.4876	13.0210	13.5795	14.1640	14.7757	15.4157	16.0853	16.7858
10	12.5779	13.1808	13.8164	14.4866	15.1929	15.9374	16.7220	17.5487	18.4197	19.3373	20.3037
11	14.2068	14.9716	15.7836	16.6455	17.5603	18.5312	19.5614	20.6546	21.8143	23.0445	24.2393
12	15.9171	16.8699	17.8885	18.9771	20.1407	21.3843	22.7132	24.1331	25.6502	27.2707	29.0017
13	17.7130	18.8821	20.1406	21.4953	22.9534	24.5227	26.2116	28.0291	29.9847	32.0887	34.3519
14	19.5986	21.0151	22.5505	24.2149	26.0192	27.9750	30.0949	32.3926	34.8827	37.5811	40.5047
15	21.5786	23.2760	25.1290	27.1521	29.3609	31.7725	34.4054	37.2797	40.4175	43.8424	47.5804
16	23.6575	25.6725	27.8881	30.3243	33.0034	35.9497	39.1899	42.7533	46.6717	50.9804	55.7175
17	25.8404	28.2129	30.8402	33.7502	36.9737	40.5447	44.5008	48.8837	53.7391	59.1176	65.0751
18	28.1324	30.9057	33.9990	37.4502	41.3013	45.5992	50.3959	55.7497	61.7251	68.3941	75.8364
19	30.5390	33.7600	37.3790	41.4463	46.0185	51.1591	56.9395	63.4397	70.7494	78.9692	88.2118
20	33.0660	36.7856	40.9955	45.7620	51.1601	57.2750	64.2028	72.0524	80.9468	91.0249	102.4436
21	35.7193	39.9927	44.8652	50.4229	56.7645	64.0025	72.2651	81.6987	92.4699	104.7684	118.8101
22	38.5052	43.3923	49.0057	55.4568	62.8733	71.4027	81.2143	92.5026	105.4910	120.4360	137.6316
23	41.4305	46.9958	53.4361	60.8933	69.5319	79.5430	91.1479	104.6029	120.2048	138.2970	159.2764
24	44.5020	50.8156	58.1767	66.7648	76.7898	88.4973	102.1742	118.1552	136.8315	158.6586	184.1678
25	47.7271	54.8645	63.2490	73.1059	84.7009	98.3471	114.4133	133.3339	155.6196	181.8708	212.7930

Appendix 1 (C)
Annuities Table

Year	5%	6%	7%	8%	9%	10%	11%	12%	13%	14%	15%
1	1.050000	1.060000	1.070000	1.080000	1.090000	1.100000	1.110000	1.120000	1.130000	1.140000	1.150000
2	0.537805	0.545437	0.553092	0.560769	0.568469	0.576190	0.583934	0.591698	0.599484	0.607290	0.615116
3	0.367209	0.374110	0.381052	0.388034	0.395055	0.402115	0.409213	0.416349	0.423522	0.430731	0.437977
4	0.282012	0.288591	0.295228	0.301921	0.308669	0.315471	0.322326	0.329234	0.336194	0.343205	0.350265
5	0.230975	0.237396	0.243891	0.250456	0.257092	0.263797	0.270570	0.277410	0.284315	0.291284	0.298316
6	0.197017	0.203363	0.209796	0.216315	0.222920	0.229607	0.236377	0.243226	0.250153	0.257157	0.264237
7	0.172820	0.179135	0.185553	0.192072	0.198691	0.205405	0.212215	0.219118	0.226111	0.233192	0.240360
8	0.154722	0.161036	0.167468	0.174015	0.180674	0.187444	0.194321	0.201303	0.208387	0.215570	0.222850
9	0.140690	0.147022	0.153486	0.160080	0.166799	0.173641	0.180602	0.187679	0.194869	0.202168	0.209574
10	0.129505	0.135868	0.142378	0.149029	0.155820	0.162745	0.169801	0.176984	0.184290	0.191714	0.199252
11	0.120389	0.126793	0.133357	0.140076	0.146947	0.153963	0.161121	0.168415	0.175841	0.183394	0.191069
12	0.112825	0.119277	0.125902	0.132695	0.139651	0.146763	0.154027	0.161437	0.168986	0.176669	0.184481
13	0.106456	0.112960	0.119651	0.126522	0.133567	0.140779	0.148151	0.155677	0.163350	0.171164	0.179110
14	0.101024	0.107585	0.114345	0.121297	0.128433	0.135746	0.143228	0.150871	0.158667	0.166609	0.174688
15	0.096342	0.102963	0.109795	0.116830	0.124059	0.131474	0.139065	0.146824	0.154742	0.162809	0.171017
16	0.092270	0.098952	0.105858	0.112977	0.120300	0.127817	0.135517	0.143390	0.151426	0.159615	0.167948
17	0.088699	0.095445	0.102425	0.109629	0.117046	0.124664	0.132471	0.140457	0.148608	0.156915	0.165367
18	0.085546	0.092357	0.099413	0.106702	0.114212	0.121930	0.129843	0.137937	0.146201	0.154621	0.163186
19	0.082745	0.089621	0.096753	0.104128	0.111730	0.119547	0.127563	0.135763	0.144134	0.152663	0.161336
20	0.080243	0.087185	0.094393	0.101852	0.109546	0.117460	0.125576	0.133879	0.142354	0.150986	0.159761
21	0.077996	0.085005	0.092289	0.099832	0.107617	0.115624	0.123838	0.132240	0.140814	0.149545	0.158417
22	0.075971	0.083046	0.090406	0.098032	0.105905	0.114005	0.122313	0.130811	0.139479	0.148303	0.157266
23	0.074137	0.081278	0.088714	0.096422	0.104382	0.112572	0.120971	0.129560	0.138319	0.147231	0.156278
24	0.072471	0.079679	0.087189	0.094978	0.103023	0.111300	0.119787	0.128463	0.137308	0.146303	0.155430
25	0.070952	0.078228	0.085811	0.093679	0.101806	0.110168	0.118740	0.127500	0.136426	0.145498	0.154699

Appendix 2

Institute of Value Management

The Secretary of IVM
Mr G. H. Parkinson
Priest House
Bisley
Gloucestershire
GL6 7BL
United Kingdom

Tel: 01452 770 287
Fax: 01452 770 252

Society of American Value Engineers

SAVE Headquarters
60 Revere Drive
Suite 500
Northbrook, IL 60062
USA

Tel: 001 (708) 480 9080
Fax: (708) 480 9282

References

Bryant, J. (1992) *Managing Value: Module II Seminar Notes*, Massachusetts, Value Management Associates.

Bythaway, C.W. (1992a) CVS, *1992 SAVE Proceedings*

Bythaway, C.W. (1992b) FAST – An Intuitive Thinking Technique, *Save Proceedings*

de Bono, E. (1992) *Serious Creativity*, New York: Manager Business.

Dell 'Isolla, A. J. (1988) Value Engineering in the Construction Industry, Washington DC: Smith, Hinchman & Grylls, 3rd Edn.

Dell 'Isolla, A. J. and S. J. Kirk (1991): *Life Cycle Costing for Design Professionals*, London: McGraw-Hill.

Drury, C. (1992) *Management and Cost Accounting*, London: Chapman & Hall, 3rd edn.

Drucker, P. (1979) *Management*, Harmondsworth: Pan Books

Ferry, D. J. O. and Flanagan, R. (1991) *Life Cycle Costing : a radical approach*, CIRIA report, 122, London: CIRIA.

Flanagan, R. and Norman, G. (1993) *Risk Management and Construction*, Oxford: Blackwell.

Green, S. D. and Popper, P. A. (1990) 'Value Engineering: The Search for Unnecessary Cost', CIOB, *occasional Paper*, 39.

Huczynski, A. A. and Buchanan, D. A. (1991) *Organizational Behaviour: An Introductory Text*, Hemel Hempstead Prentice-Hall, 2nd edn.

Kelly, J. and Male, S. (1993) *Value Management in Design and Construction*, London: E & F. N. Spon.

Kuhn, R. K. (1988) *Handbook for Creative and Innovative Managers*, New York: McGraw-Hill.

Miles, L. D. (1972) *Techniques of Value Analysis and Engineering* New York: McGraw-Hill.

O'Brien, J. (1976) *Value Analysis in Design and Construction*, New York: McGraw-Hill.

Osborn, A. F. (1963) *Applied Imagination: Principles and Procedures of Creative Problem Solving*, New York: Scribner.

Seeley, I. H. (1983) *Building Economics*, London: Macmillan, 3rd edn.

Sperling, R. B., CVS, *1993 SAVE Proceedings*.

Sperling, R. B. (1993) *The PDQs of FAST: Simplifying Function Analysis for Construction Value Studies*, SAVE Proceedings, International Conference.

SPRINT (1992) *The European Market for Value Analysis*, Luxembourg Commission of the European Communities.

Zimmerman, L.W. and Hart, G. D. (1982) *Value Engineering: A practical approach for owners, designers and constructors*. New York: Van Nostrand Reinhold.

Index